Literary Dundee is the home of all things creative in Dundee - books, films, reading, writing and poetry. We publish New Writing Dundee and we're partners in the Dundee International Book Prize.

We are also involved with literary salons, the Dundee Literary Festival, author talks, poetry readings, Saturday Evening Lecture Series and much more.

Get involved in Creative Writing classes - either as part of the University of Dundee or our Festival Writing School.

For more information on all of this, or to sign up for Literary Dundee updates, email *literarydundee@gmail.com* or join the Literary Dundee group on Facebook.

For information on classes contact *k.j.gunn@dundee.ac.uk.*

Our website is updated regularly - *www.literarydundee.co.uk* – please check it out.

Anna Day
Director Literary Dundee

New Writing Dundee Volume 5

Edited by: Rachel Marsh and Amy Kinmond
Contributing Editor: Kirsty Gunn

Selection Editors:
Hazel Ellis-Saxon
Tamara Girardi
Kathleen Gray
Juliana Janisch
Sam Longden
Paul McFadyen
Samira Nadkarni
Sheila Reid
Clare Skelton
Edward Small
Jacqueline Thompson
Rebecca Varian
Zoe Venditozzi

Copyeditor: Georgina Quinn

Special thanks to School of Humanities, University of Dundee.

We would also like to thank the Creative Writing and English Departments, University of Dundee.

Published by: Discovery Press
Printed by: Robertson Printers, Forfar
Edited by: Rachel Marsh and Amy Kinmond
Design and Layout by: Martin Rowbottom
Cover Art by: Sam Longden

Typeface: Century Schoolbook
ISBN: 978-1-84586-096-7

New Writing Dundee
Five

To my best Phriend on her birthday,
and celebrating the occasion of being
30 years Best Phriends!

Ph4e

Heather
xx.

Contents

New Writing Dundee – Foreword 2010

In these straitened times it makes more sense than ever to champion and celebrate the role small publications play in literary and cultural life. As conservatism creeps in to dampen down arts funding, when safe 'bets' are backed over wild and experimental ventures, when literature itself is proscribed by marketing plans and 'what the public wants', originality crippled by 'playing it safe' in order to keep the sales figures healthy... Well, this is the time to sound the trumpets and bring out a new issue of New Writing Dundee!

In our brand new 2010 issue, Editor Rachel Marsh and her team have done everything they can to say 'Boo!' to the Recession. Here are stories that buck trends and tell new tales, that are peculiar and idiosyncratic and wonderful, told in a range of voices and styles that will surprise you. Here are poems that twist into strange little metaphors that are scattered like fizz bombs and sparklers through the pages. Here are fragments, pieces, an interview – and everywhere: ideas!

Of course we have our usual, gorgeous eclectic mixture of new and seasoned writers, brand new names sitting alongside internationally recognised prize winners like Christopher Reid, Vincent O'Sullivan, Adam Mars Jones and Robert Crawford. Where else but in New Writing Dundee do first time writers get to display their work like this, in such auspicious company? And where but here might recognised authors graciously sit alongside an utterly unknown name?

Yet the fact that everything comes together this way describes everything about our Literary Life at Dundee – a generous, spirited, informed community that is open and alive to new ways of doing things, that treats a cultural life as one that is available to all, not just a few. So we bring the world to Dundee - with our Literary Salons' and Festival's tip top line up of famous authors and poets and agents. So in turn we send our students and writers out across the Tay – to publish and work in Edinburgh, Glasgow, London and New York...And welcome them home again.

And so, too, despite the press of the economy, New Writing Dundee will thrive and grow. Read it, write for it, share it. There is much to be proud of, here in this new issue.

Kirsty Gunn
Professor of Writing
University of Dundee

Come Again?
Family Shots
Convent Girl in the Wairarapa
Three Poems by Vincent O'Sullivan

Come Again?

There was a poem she read so far back
it was the days when halter tops
were the thing, or a skirt you'd see now
only on kids done up for a party

taking the micky from the olds.
It had struck her as over the top in the way
that kind of poetry often was: every
heartbeat thrown there larger than

life, you're waiting to say 'ah!' at the big
screen, 'this is life when romance is given
a fair run.' Stars back it up,
nature thrumming away with its hot

guitars. Never quite her thing.
But that line after all these years –
'My solitude,' it more or less went,
'churning its arms like a swimmer hanging on.

Vincent O'Sullivan
Family Shots

Loved it, leaning on old
knees, looking, 'At the farm
with your Gran,' 'There's your
mother at Waiuk. Her

with the thin arms!' Always
back, further back the better,
parents in short pants,
funny old togs to swim in.

Before colour photos.
Now the push at your own
knee, 'Don't turn it yet!'
'But you never said your hair

grew long as that!'
'Whiskers, what did they
call them? Sideboards,
really, did they?'

'But if that's his best suit
why's he wearing it
there? Getting so sick
I mean, why's he so dressed up?'

But they did in those days.
To have the suit handy
when it came to laying out.
'But we burn them now

though, don't we?
Always?' Just about.
Lean on your knees, then,
can we? Look at some more?

Convent Girl in the Wairarapa

She knew about saints and he didn't.
She put her heels on the dashboard
and they worked at having a good time
and the gear-lever was an awkward joke

before they settled neatly to it,
then it was fine, the past generations
one with them in spirit, the moral
imperative, shall we say, on hold,

and excuses, between themselves,
the future's happy to accept. They
work themselves to a lather, Wednesdays
after squash. And after the white wind's

catching her veil at St Antony's
on a winter afternoon she says, 'Patron
of lepers and farmers, know that, do you?'
God, he adored her! Saturday's bride.

Auckland born Vincent O'Sullivan is a poet, fiction writer, dramatist, academic and editor. O'Sullivan has received numerous distinguished awards, residencies and fellowships, and his writing has been widely published nationally and internationally. His verse is collected in Revenants (1969), Bearings (1973), From the Indian Funeral (1976), Butcher & Co. (1977), Brother Jonathan, Brother Kafka (1979), The Rose Ballroom and Other Poems (1982), The Butcher Papers (1982), The Pilate Tapes (1986) and Selected Poems (1992). O'Sullivan has co-edited five volumes of The Collected Letters of Katherine Mansfield, as well as various other scholarly texts. In 2006, he was honoured for his poetry at the New Zealand Prime Ministers Awards for Literary Achievement.

Irrational Fear of Tom Stoppard
By Adam Mars-Jones

Bourne End in Buckinghamshire was always a desirable place to live, even in the 1950s when Mum and Dad moved us there, and the Abbotsbrook Estate was certainly the nicest part. An ordinary house near the river could cost ten thousand pounds even then — well out of their reach. Dad was still in the Air Force, earning less than £2,000 a year, while Mum had only done a little nursing before I was born, and had no plans to go back. They were both sick of service housing, but Abbotsbrook would only have been a dream — if they hadn't spotted a house that was so neglected it was like something out of a fairy tale.

The garden was completely overgrown and there was no electricity. Two half-blind old ladies were living there, sisters, managing to cook in a kitchen encrusted with grease but not to clean up after themselves. They only wanted three thousand for the place, and Mum and Dad made up their minds right away.

There was a lot of work to be done, inside and out, and to start with we camped there (as Mum said) 'like gypsies'. Like happy gypsies.

My brother Peter and I loved the smell of the paraffin lamps, and were quite disappointed when they were replaced by electric lights, which seemed like dead things by comparison. I must have been seven and Peter was five. The new telephone was a disappointment too, since it didn't have a little voice in it saying 'number please?' like the one in the old house. You just made the number with your fingers.

When the house was finished it looked quite different. In the old ladies' time it had been called St Dunstan's, but Mum and Dad changed the name to Trees. This was a new start for all of us, why not the house as well? Our nearest neighbour Arthur Hand, who knew his way round a box of paints, did a portrait of the restored house in oils and was kind enough to present us with it.

It was all a big step up socially, especially for Mum. In the company of other service wives she had been something of a queen bee, but she felt the strain of her new surroundings. She would explain to strangers that we didn't live 'on an estate' — which would mean that the Council was our landlord — but 'on the Estate'. The Abbotsbrook Estate, where top people lived.

It was a godsend when Arthur's wife Muriel invited Mum to join her sewing circle. Sewing wasn't the main business of the group, which was really gossip, but Mum shone as a needlewoman and dressmaker. Muriel recommended her to friends, and soon Mum had a little money coming in. Before long we even had a cleaning lady, who really did live on an estate, with the Council as her landlord.

Another friendly neighbour was an actor called Jon Pertwee. If Peter and I had known he was a future Doctor Who we would have treated him as a holy and spectacular being — except that Doctor Who had yet to be thought of. It was not yet time for the lord of time.

Jon Pertwee was entirely approachable, and younger than we had originally thought, since when we first met he had his hair dusted grey for a role. He told us to call him Poetry — not Pertwee but Poetry.

Poetry was the life and soul of any party. Mum and Dad told us about one riverside gala at which Jon Pertwee had rowed an abandoned boat until it sank, then swam ashore fully clothed to wild applause.

Jon Pertwee didn't intimidate Mum because he knew how to butter her up, saying what a gem the house was and to be sure and tell him if we ever wanted to sell.

I think it was through Jon Pertwee that Bourne End was chosen as the location for a film — The Pumpkin Eater, starring Peter Finch. That must have been in 1963 or 4.

By and large Bourne End enjoyed its walk-on role in British cinema history. The only complication of the shoot was that one elderly resident turned out not to have signed the release prepared by the production company. She refused to take direction, and would trot out of her front door, innocently or not, whenever the cameras rolled, perhaps aiming for a walk-on part all her own.

I didn't know that Peter Finch was a film star. All I knew was that I had never seen an adult squat on his heels for so long at a time. He seemed to shift his weight very gradually from side to side. When I asked him how he had learned this trick, he explained that he was originally from Australia, and had taught himself by watching the Aborigines there. They could squat like that all day.

Peter Finch offered to give Peter and me a ride in his enormous car, but Mum wouldn't let us go. I don't think she was alarmed by him, though, it was just the old rule about not accepting lifts from strange men, which applied even to strange film stars.

Of course Peter Finch was only a bird of passage, but celebrities continued to trickle into Bourne End at a modest rate. Michael Aspel, the television and radio personality, was probably the most famous resident, though he didn't actually live on the Abbotsbrook Estate. Mum wasn't keen on the idea of meeting Michael Aspel, but she wasn't cowed by the prospect either. After all, putting people at their ease was pretty much what he did for a living. Sometimes I'd see her adjusting the lie of her scarf in the hall mirror before she left the house, taking a deep breath as if she was going on stage, but in general her nerves held steady.

Then one day at the sewing circle, over coffee and biscuits, she heard some news that knocked her right off her perch. A young and successful playwright was moving to the Abbotsbrook Estate with his wife Jose (was that pronounced Josie? Muriel wondered) and small son. Tom Stoppard. From what the other women were saying, he was one of the most brilliant writers in the country. Mum had always been intimidated by conspicuously clever people, and the news of this new arrival only a few hundred yards from her front door was quite a blow to her confidence.

There were regular bulletins at the sewing circle about the illustrious new resident. The Stoppards had bought a large thatched house by the river, with a Victorian boathouse, also thatched, where the great man went to write. It was on a tiny island of its own, reached across a little bridge.

Bourne End was pleased to have been chosen by this young literary lion as his personal safari park. His immediate neighbours had only one complaint. Stoppard had bought peacocks, perhaps assuming with his playwright's imagination that they would stay decoratively put, like stage props. They didn't. They went a-wandering. Sometimes they pecked. Their eerie cries carried surprisingly far.

Mum's concern wasn't with Stoppard's livestock but the simple threat of his presence. She couldn't get it out of her head that this formidably clever person was living so near to her. She could feel his brain working unstoppably, while she tried to concentrate on her library book. It was as if that brain was an oversized appliance draining the National Grid, siphoning off what little power she could muster. And if he made her feel so stupid when he was still so far off, what would it be like if they were ever in the same room? She couldn't bear to think about it. A plume of intellectual radiation was drifting across Bourne End, and she was the only one who knew it.

Soon things got so bad that Mum couldn't leave the house to go shopping. She would put on her scarf and pick up her basket, but then she wouldn't be able to get past the door. She would sit on a chair in the hall for hours, trying to summon up courage. Dad tried to get her to snap out of it, but she just broke down. What if she was at the butcher's or the greengrocer's, and then turned round and saw Tom Stoppard next to her in the queue? She would die, that's what. She knew what he looked like — his picture had been in the local papers. What was she supposed to do if he spoke to her, shaking his tousled mop of hair, grinning at her with his vast white teeth, scattering epigrams and philosophical conundrums in all directions?

We tried to tell her that famous playwrights don't do their own shopping. She was perfectly safe. Had she actually seen him in the Bourne End shops ever? She was adamant that she had glimpsed him once coming out of the off-licence. He had seemed to be surfing off the premises on a wave of highbrow laughter. We tried to explain the difference between picking up a bottle of wine on your way to a dinner party and queuing up for pork chops at the butcher's, but she wouldn't have it.

I was a teenager by then, not far short of my A-levels, and I did my best to help. I borrowed 'Rosencrantz and Guildenstern Are Dead' from the Bourne End Library and read it on the sly. Then I tried to tell Mum that Tom Stoppard wasn't really that clever, but she wouldn't be comforted. She could tell my heart wasn't in it. She knew me too well to be fooled by good intentions.

It reached a point where Mum could hardly nerve herself to go to Muriel's sewing circle. Peter and I would act as a sort of human shield while she walked the short distance, screening her from exposure to harmful brainwaves. Even then she was frightened. What if he — she didn't say the name — was having trouble writing a play and went for a walk to seek inspiration? He might appear round the corner, with an escort of peacocks making their strangled-baby cry, spreading his own great tail of blue-green wisdom wide, until the light sparkled from all the eyes of his mind. What if he started firing witticisms at her unprovoked?

When we had delivered Mum to Muriel's we had to promise to come back and collect her in a couple of hours. Then one day Dad found her mixing up a pail of whitewash in the kitchen. She was going to paint over the windows, to protect us all against the catastrophic flash from Stoppard's brain. It was civil defence, civil self-defence. Dad spoke to her soothingly for once, as he poured the whitewash away. It was only later that he expressed his own tension, saying he was near the end of his rope with the whole bloody business. There was fear on Peter's face, perhaps on mine too.

We were beginning to wonder if it was even a good idea for Mum to go to Muriel's any more. In a way it was her life-line, more necessary than it had ever been, but it was also a place where she was highly likely to hear news of the radiant thinking machine which stopped her from sleeping.

Eventually, though, it was at Muriel's that she had the first news of deliverance. The bush telegraph of Bourne End was all of a twitter. Jose Stoppard had started to behave strangely after the birth of another son. She had made rather a scene at the chemist's, shouting that it was she who had written the plays which had made her husband famous.

Mum wasn't the sort to take pleasure in another woman's troubles, and marital breakdown was still a troubling rarity in her circle. Even so she had a sense of consolation, of reprieve. It was tragic that a crack in the core of that nuclear brain, some defect in its shielding, had exposed an innocent party to toxic overdose, but at least it meant — surely — that the danger to the public would be taken seriously. Then she wouldn't be alone any more. This wasn't a case of estrangement but contamination, radiation sickness in its marital form.

Later bulletins confirmed the fact of breakdown. Late in 1969 Tom Stoppard moved out, taking his sons with him, and put Thatch End on the market. Mum began to breathe more easily. Her world returned to something like normal. She still had the rituals she needed to perform before leaving the house, rapping softly with her knuckles on either side of the hall mirror in patterns of five and eleven. But then she could do her chores. She could get some joy, even, from going shopping.

One day she met Michael Aspel in the newsagent's and wasn't in the least put off. They nattered as if they'd known each other all their lives. They had a rare old chinwag.

Adam Mars-Jones was named one of Granta's 'Best Young British Novelists' in 1993 when his first novel The Waters of Thirst was published. He has been a film critic for The Independent and The Times, is an occasional contributor to The Guardian and the Times Literary Supplement, and a regular reviewer for The Observer. Adam has three collections of short stories, the first of which was the winner of a Somerset Maugham Award. He also has a collection of essays entitled Blind Bitter Happiness. His most recent novel Pilcrow is the first in a series of four and has been short-listed for the Encore Award.

Sunburst Finish

By Andy Jackson

For him, just fourteen years, the book came first,
A Christmas gift from quiet Uncle Jack.
Bert Weedon, virtuoso king of strings,
beard-wearer of the year in '56,
grinning from the frontispiece.
Play In A Day? The lying bastard.

His piggy bank grew fat on paper rounds,
until the shop exchanged his gold for wood
and stainless steel, the maple body
glowing on the racking in the darkened store.
Money talks. His said goodbye, but waved
as he departed with the flight case on his back.

The case stood in the shadows in the spare room
every night, as stern as Johnny Cash,
nearly-black with alligator flesh,
silver buckled waist and streaks of sweat,
thick white stitching down each shoulder,
gaunt and watchful as a crow.

He learned some chords, but couldn't play
the tunes his daughter knew, her blood so weak
from isotopes towards the end, the charts
once bright but now so full of junk. The case
had shrunk but still he hoovered round it every week,
a snake-skinned coffin, too small for a man
but large enough to carry children from this world.

Andy Jackson was born in Manchester in 1965 but moved to Scotland in 1992. His poems have appeared in New Writing Scotland, New Writing Dundee, Eric, Riverrun, Poetry News, Poetry Scotland and on various online poetry sites, and he was winner of the National Galleries of Scotland creative writing competition in 2008. His first collection The Assassination Museum was published by Red Squirrel in March 2010.

The Amazing Headless Woman
By K. F. Gray

I remember it like this, a day in the summer of 1965, a child's summer when every day was bright and unmade. Our dear Aunt Billo had come to take us to Aikey Fair, and I was filled to the brim with excitement. We lived on a farm and neither my dour father, nor my tethered mother, would take a day off their work, amidst the kirn and dubs, to enjoy themselves, and so it was left to my Aunt to take us, my sister and I, to the Fair.

Aunt Billo was both ugly and glamorous. She was tall and heavy, not fat, but what would kindly be called, 'big boned'. She wore a beautiful floral dress drawn in at the waist with a flared skirt that came to just below her knees. She wore nylons, (these being the days before tights), which meant she kept them up with a suspender belt – an unmentionable adult word, like knickers and brassiere. She wore strappy sandals and a white, nylon cardigan, which I thought very grand because it had a label and had been bought in a shop. All my cardigans were knitted by my other aunts

– Billo, didn't knit – and were made from itchy wool and were worn
both in summer and winter. Billo wore clip-on earrings and a
silver watch. Her hair was a dull brown and she wore it in tightly
permed curls. She had thick rimmed glasses perched on a huge
nose, the Penny nose, which all the girls in the family seemed
unfortunately to have inherited. Billo was unmarried and worked
as a short-hand typist in an office in Aberdeen. She rented rooms
in the Broomhill area, and I wanted to be like her when I grew up.

    The Fair was held on the hillside above a stream. Aunt Billo told
us the story of how, a long time ago, a travelling tinker had fallen
into the river and had set out his wares to dry on the river banks.
Some local people saw his things and thought he had set them out
for sale and went to buy them. The tinker saw a good business
opportunity and sold everything he had and promised to come back
the following year with more goods. This he did and so apparently
the Fair developed into a large gathering, over a couple of days
where everything was traded, including horses. Now, the Fair was
a gaudy collection of merry-go-rounds, shooting galleries and stalls
selling toffee apples. There was a boxing ring, a hall of mirrors and
a flea circus.

    We went to the Fair by bus. The day was sticky and hot and
already the tar was blistering on the road as we walked the mile to
the bus stop at the Half Way House pub. Climbing the steps of the
bus, looking out of the window, admiring the clippie with her beehive
of blonde hair and pink lipstick – these were all exotic activities for
me. Aunt Billo sat in front of us, fanning herself with her clutch
handbag.

    The bus dropped us at the entrance of the Fair, and we were, all
at once, in the middle of the crowd. I was a child who was happy
to look rather than take part, as was my sister, so we were easy
to please. The dodgem cars were too violent for us, the ghost train
too unknown; about the only thing we tried was to hook the plastic
ducks with the number on their underbellies. The number corre-
sponded to a prize, but we didn't win anything. Aunt Billo bought
us wonderful, gauzy wide brimmed hats to keep off the sun. Mine
was yellow, my sister's blue. We had our photo taken with a vicious,
little monkey sitting on my shoulder. He wore a waistcoat and a top

hat and had razor-sharp teeth. We are not smiling in the photo, but I was happy, so very happy to be here in this place of miracles and magic.

We had circled the Fair from the outside and now found ourselves in the centre where a big tent had been erected. The board outside the entrance proclaimed 'the most amazing sight on earth – a headless woman'. The price was a steep one shilling but since we had been lenient on the other rides Aunt Billo agreed we should see this remarkable claim.

'How does she eat, aunty? How does she hear? Can she smell?'

The next show was in fifteen minutes, and we queued to get our tickets.

A man with a bow tie and a microphone walked on stage and shouted, 'Now, for a miracle in science, the most incredible sight you will ever see, the one and only, Lorraine, the headless woman. Come on out, Lorraine.'

Nothing happened, the stage remained empty and I looked up at Billo, who was staring straight ahead. Still no one appeared and the man on stage began to look around and smile nervously at the audience.

'Lorraine, come on out. These people have paid good money to see you. Don't be shy.'

Still nothing, and now people began to shift in their seats and glance at each other. One or two whispered. 'Maybe she had died,' I remember thinking. It was quite serious, I knew, to be without your head.

'One moment, ladies and gentlemen.'

The man went behind the curtains and flicked them dramatically behind him. We waited. The audience collectively held their breath and then the man re-emerged from behind the red curtain holding the hand of a woman. We gasped. He pulled at the woman's arm and then, there she was, Lorraine, the headless woman, in full view for everyone to see.

The headless lady was petite with an orange mini-skirt, a green long sleeved top and brown knee length boots. Where her head should have been was a metal cylinder with some large holes in it and huge amounts of cotton wool appeared out of the top of it and underneath, covering her neck. A couple of tubes sprouted from the cylinder but they were not attached to anything and simply stopped in mid air. The headless lady flailed her arms around as if trying to get her balance.

The man with the microphone looked triumphantly at the audience.

'Lorraine, can you hear me? Nod your head for yes and shake it for no.'

No one in the audience moved. The headless Lorraine nodded. He then proceeded to ask her a variety of questions while Lorraine turned her head sightlessly from side to side. We discovered she'd lost her head in an accident with a lorry. We heard how the surgeons had worked round the clock to perform the life saving operation she needed to live without a head. We learned that she was not in any pain and, perhaps, I was just a little disappointed not to see some blood. Surely a headless woman would be covered in it?

Although there had been a promise that the audience could ask any questions, the man with the microphone abruptly ended the show after only five minutes because not having a head was very tiring, and Lorraine needed to get some rest. We were assured that doctors were standing by. The red curtains were pulled and gradually the audience began to blink and stretch and mutter.

I sat for a long time watching the folds of the curtain come to stillness and then Aunt Billo was calling me from the end of the row of seats.

'Come on, let's get a candy floss.'

Usually a sweet would be enough to tempt me, but I was reluctant to leave. I had seen a headless woman, and I fizzed with the knowledge of this extraordinary privilege. Then my sister wanted the toilet, and we had to climb up the side of the hill to crouch behind some boulders to relieve ourselves. The tent looked miniature from our position, and I wondered who took the headless lady to the toilet, for surely, she would need some help, wouldn't she?

The hot, humid afternoon gave way to a dark, growling sky, and Aunt Billo decided that it was time to catch the bus home before we got soaked. We should have known better, but optimistically we had set off without our coats, so by the time we got back to the farm house we were thoroughly soaked in the downpour. Our fine-looking hats were a crumpled mass of fabric, Aunt Billo's sandals were spoiled, and her nylons ripped; her hair was ruined and we were all shivering.

'Why didn't you come and meet us with the car?' Aunt Billo asked my father.

'I don't have time for that silly nonsense. It's your own fault you're wet,' was the reply.

I never saw my Aunt Billo after that day. There was a terrible argument between her and my father about the walk home in the rain, and he told her never to come back to the farm again.

What I don't remember about that shimmering day was telling my mother or father about the headless lady we'd seen at Aikey Fair. And they never asked.

K F Gray has published a number of short stories and poems since completing her M Litt in creative writing at St Andrews University in 2005. As well as pursuing her own writing, Kathleen teaches ESOL and facilitates a writing workshop in Dundee. She is currently working on a novel on the theme of forgiveness. Kathleen enjoys long beach and hill walks with her Border Collie.

Leaving the Emerald City
By Paul McFadyen

I drop the sun
like a
sack
of
sand
into
the desert.

My balloon shoots up
as a soul to firmament,
streaking past
emerald stars
shining like faces.

Paul McFadyen is from Dundee. He is in his early-mid-twenties. He hopes that you enjoy his poem.

Little Angels

By Paul Gorman

C hloe snapped the thin elastic of the witch's hat against her chin. She screwed up her face.

'If the wind changes, you'll stay like that,' said Yvonne, her mother, pulling into shape the collar of her daughter's gown.

'Like what?'

'Like this.' Yvonne made a face and tickled her under the arms. Chloe squirmed.

'It's not true,' she giggled.

'There's only one way to find out.'

Chloe glanced out of the window for signs of the changing wind but it was dark, of course. It was almost November.

'Okay Griselda,' said Yvonne, switching the hallway light on as they left the flat, let's go and visit the little devil.

Yvonne didn't like Millie. She suspected the child would grow up to be trouble. But the two girls were inseparable, and Yvonne couldn't, if asked, define what it was about the girl that unsettled her. She didn't distrust Millie, or disapprove of her behaviour, or fear for Chloe's morals, yet the feeling she cultivated contained a nugget of all these. But she had uncovered nothing in what Chloe said, or what she could sift from the talk of other parents, to justify her suspicion. She thought back to the troublesome kids she had known at school. With some children, you could tell early on that it wouldn't take much of a change in the wind for them to turn out bad. She tried to project Millie some years - ten, maybe - into the future. The images her unconscious mind constructed were not healthy. But there was nothing except her own imaginings to stop her daughter associating with the girl. And she said nothing to Chloe.

They climbed the endless stairs to the tenement flat where Millie's parents lived. Yvonne had never met either of them and was eager for an idea of the girl's background. After a long wait the door opened, revealing Millie, also dressed as a witch but wearing a mask. The hallway wasn't much warmer than the stairwell, and a lone bulb emitted a sickly yellow light. Chloe and Millie immediately fell to in girlish gossip. Yvonne followed her daughter across the threshold.

The grim reaper, dressed all in black and with a grimacing skull under a heavy-looking hood, closed the door behind them. Yvonne jumped.

'Hello Chloe.' It spoke with a woman's voice. Chloe spun round to see where the voice came from.

'Hello!'

'Chloe's very welcome: she's a little angel. You must be very proud of her.'

'Thank you. I'm Yvonne. Are you Millie's mother?'

Laughter behind the mask, though the grimace remained. I am Death, the final reckoner.

'Mum!' Millie giggled.

Yvonne forced a smile.

The reaper showed them into a large living room, from which burst the noise of children at play. Mille gave Chloe a spare mask. Everyone was wearing a mask; everyone but Yvonne.

'You're welcome to stay,' said the reaper, in a voice which Yvonne suspected meant the opposite. 'You aren't wearing a mask?'

'No,' said Yvonne. 'I don't like - it's the proximity thing. Like being stuck in a lift.'

Death merely nodded, and left the room. The reaper, Yvonne and a tall, very thin man dressed as a black cat, appeared to be the only adults in attendance. Yvonne wondered if this was within Safety Guidelines for a party of its size. Weren't there rules?

When Death reappeared, she was offering a bottle of red wine and a glass.

'Thank you.'

A hand – reassuringly fleshy and pink – poured until the glass was full. The bottle, Yvonne noticed, was dusty, and the wine strong. She made a polite cough; a low chuckle replied from behind the mask.

'Good wine.'

'A good vintage,' said the skull.

Yvonne looked around the room. There must have been at least twenty children, among them several witches and two, Yvonne couldn't help but feel, shoddy ghosts, who had evidently had an old bed-spread thrown over them by way of fancy dress. They darted about the room and chased each other in twos and threes. The windows of the room were blacked out with crepe paper. At the back was what seemed to be a wardrobe, shrouded by a dustsheet. From the ceiling spiders and bats hung on long pieces of thread, as did cardboard silhouettes of evilly grinning pumpkins and skulls. These swung as the children brushed them. The motion made Yvonne feel giddy. She clutched her glass.

She continued to sip while the black cat nudged the door open. His movements effortless despite the evident weight, he presented a large plastic basin which swam with a dark liquid and in which long-stemmed apples bobbed. Yvonne grinned, delighted that such games still took place at children's parties. He set it down and the children dropped to their knees; Chloe and Millie rubbed shoulders.

Child after child, after first removing their masks, dipped their faces into the water. Most, though not all, managed to snag an apple stalk between their teeth. Chloe, Yvonne was pleased to note, was successful.

'Would you like to try?' the cat asked, his voice as soft as the velvet bodysuit he wore. Yvonne hadn't noticed him slinking alongside her.

'Me?' The children had all finished. One or two, Yvonne noticed, regarded the apples with suspicion and distaste. Some - Chloe among them - munched on theirs, a few of which still hung in the water of the basin.

'Yes. When was the last time you dunked for apples?'

'Twenty years ago, at least.'

'Well, then.'

As the wine made itself at home, the idea seemed appealing.

'Okay. She got down on her knees.'

'Hands behind your back now,' cautioned the cat. The children, Chloe among them, watched eagerly. There was no malice in their faces, but each, Yvonne was certain, willed her – an adult – to fail.

The water was icy cold. The apples moved away as she angled her face towards them. The hard spheres of the fruit knocked against nose and brow and cheekbone. She opened her mouth, teeth slightly apart to clamp a passing apple-stalk. If she could just grip the sides of the basin.

No sooner was the thought formed than her hands moved. Instantly, she felt them grabbed and held tight together behind her back. The shock made her bite and she caught the inside of her cheek. With a cry she pulled her face from the water. Her captor relinquished his grip.

'You cheated,' said the cat.

Yvonne cupped her mouth, her face dripping red to the carpet.

'It's a game, for f...' she stopped, seeing the little masked faces all around her. 'For crying out loud. I'm bleeding.'

'It's just coloured water,' said the cat, picking up the basin.

'I said I'm bleeding. Where's the bathroom?'

'Follow me.'

The reaper announced the next entertainment as Yvonne was led from the room.

'Who wants to see a vanishing trick?'

The closing door muffled the children's affirmations. The cat stood in the kitchen doorway, blocking Yvonne's view.

'Bathroom is round the corner, at the end of the hall.'

'Thank you,' Yvonne muttered, poking at the wound with her tongue.

The bathroom door was locked, and she waited her turn. She could hear what sounded like chanting from the children, followed by a cheer; time and again it came, as if at some recurring event, its spectacle undimmed by repetition. Finally the bathroom door opened and one of the children emerged. He ran past Yvonne and through to join his companions.

Yvonne locked the door behind her. Again, a bare bulb cast an unflattering glow on a grimy, dust-covered room. There was a smell of damp. She was going to have to say something to Chloe.

She examined the inside of her cheek as best she could in the mirror. She dabbed at it, testing for blood. She could have sworn she'd tasted its bitterness. Whatever, there was none now.

She left the bathroom to hear another crescendo of cheering from the party. Curious, she hurried along the corridor and slipped back inside the door. She retrieved her wine and stood next to the watching cat.

The lights were down low, yet the room seemed somehow larger. The cupboard at the back of the room had been unveiled. Death stood by it, holding open the door. Standing inside was one of the bedsheet-covered ghosts. The door was closed and the reaper turned to the watching crowd.

'What are the magic words?' Death asked.

A chorus rang out from the assembled children.

'Torith! Torith! Tasna! Clova!'

Death turned the handle of the cupboard door and, with a flourish, pulled it open. The cupboard was empty. A delighted shriek from the children. Yvonne couldn't help but join in with the applause.

'Very impressive, she said to the cat. Where do they come out?'

The cat stared straight ahead, its attention not leaving the performance at the far end of the room.

'They don't, he said.'

Very funny, thought Yvonne, as she watched the next child step into the wardrobe. Once again, the rhythmic chant.

'Torith! Torith! Tasna! Clova!'

Again, the reaper opened the door to the bare wood of an empty cupboard.

Her glass empty, Yvonne set it down on the floor and realised she could see underneath the wardrobe to the back wall. She watched until the next time the incantation was chanted, but no feet emerged from the back of the wardrobe. As she stood up, it took her a few moments to realise her earlier error. The room wasn't larger; it was emptier.

'Is there a door behind the cupboard?'

But the cat was ignoring her.

She went back into the hall, past the kitchen and round the corner. She stood at the spot on the wall where, she guessed, the wardrobe must be. She pressed her ear to the wall and listened. She heard the next volunteer step into the wardrobe, heard the chanting, the creak as the door was opened, and the subsequent applause. No footsteps had left the cupboard. She hurried back to the room. The cat stood in the hallway, one paw on a hip, a glass of blood-red wine sloshing in the other.

'Is something the matter?'

'What's going on? Where have those kids gone?'

'Away,' he said simply. He raised the glass to his lips. Yvonne pushed past him. The wine spilled, wetting her and splashing the wall. He let out a yelp, for all the world like a miaow.

She burst into the room, looking around for Chloe. A movement at the other end of the room caught her eye. Someone stepping into the cupboard, their witch's hat askew.

'Bye, Mummy!' Chloe waved frantically, an eager grin on her face. The door closed on her. All around Yvonne rose the enthusiastic chanting of a spellbound crowd.

'Torith! Torith! Tasna! Clova!'

Paul Gorman's work has previously appeared in New Writing Dundee, several issues of New Writing Scotland, as well as 'Pulp.net', Cutting Teeth, Read This! among others, and he was shortlisted for the 2002 Dundee Book Prize. Originally from Fife, he studied at Dundee University and lives in Midlothian with his wife and son.

The Mute Saint
By Gordon Darroch

D anny had found the book in the library. In all his years on
the dole it was the one place that had never turned him
away. It was the poor man's cinema, a place to hang out on
Tuesdays and Wednesdays when the money was dwindling and he
needed to ration his supply of fags. Plus, some of those books were a
revelation. Especially the science ones. He didn't understand all of
the words, and still less all those equations with their squinty lines
and x's and y's and decimal points, but he loved the sense of discovery
they were infused with. He devoured books on Galileo and Newton
and Copernicus, but his favourite was Einstein.

What Danny was really searching for, and he confessed it freely,
was spiritual guidance. Science, religion, the weekend football
results: they were all paths to enlightenment. He believed, as an
article of faith, that one day he would find the book that would
bring his jumbled knowledge into alignment with a sharp click. A
book that would be like a bible to him, though without the plagues
of locusts and stoning for adulterers and other bits he was wary of.

And then one day he saw it, lying on a table, a plain white cover
with a stone figure shaped like a jelly baby on the cover wearing
what looked like a dressing-gown. As soon as he saw that blessed
image, he knew this was the inspiration he had been searching for
all these years.

*

In 1351, the hilltop town of Fiesole in Tuscany, its position already
weakened by geography and plague, was ravaged afresh by disease.
The outbreak was especially cruel for interfering with the people's
efforts to revitalise a community which in ten years had shrunk to
less than two-fifths of its former size. Worse, most of the dead were
children: first they would come out in blotchy rashes, before succumb-
ing to a severe fever, usually within a week.

In desperation some of the townsmen, many of them fathers
whose children had perished, formed a band of Flagellants and
went to the highest point on the hill. They made whips from the
hides of horses and stripped themselves of everything save their
shoes. Then, in time to the beat of a drum, they lashed themselves
across the back, stomach, arms, legs and genitals, crying out to
God for forgiveness with every stroke. They performed twenty
rounds of lashes, in strict rotation of the body parts, and concluded
by raising their whips in their right hands and reciting a long
prayer imploring the Lord to vouchsafe the well-being of the
community. Then they descended the hill and forbade their women
from tending to their wounds until three days had passed.

On the third day, a stranger appeared in the town. His skin was
pale, his body seemed horribly vast and misshapen, and his outland-
ish costume was woven from a fabric never seen before. Some people, fearing he might be the incarnation of the devil or an assassin
sent to settle a debt, bundled him up in a sackcloth and took him
to the bodega. But the man seemed incapable of speech, or had
otherwise taken a vow of silence. By complex gestures he succeeded in communicating to the elders that he wished to visit the
sick infants in the town. And so he was brought to a house where
a child was suffering from the infection. He went into the child's
room and produced a vial which – in the words of the elder – was
made of a substance unlike any other in this world, both hard and

light at the same time. He dived his hand into it and brought forth
a clutch of tiny shimmering stones. He placed two in the child's
mouth and handed the remainder to the child's mother, instructing
her to repeat the ritual for the next seven days. The child recovered
unscathed, as did thirty-six other children visited by the mysterious
healer that year. Not once did he utter a word.

*

In a cafe overlooking a disused car park two men in contrasting suits
were making fumbling efforts at conversation. One was Danny. The
flow of his speech was hampered by the large plate of chips he was
devouring with the eagerness of a snake that had just chanced on a
hamster's nest. Even so, he was the one doing most of the talking.
Steven sat opposite him, flipping an orange between his hands and
occasionally flicking his lank black hair backwards over his ear. He
watched Danny with an unspeakable disgust that expressed itself
in the crinkles of his face.

'See this guy Saint Sebastian?' spluttered Danny through a
mesh of soft potato, flapping his arms like a shot seagull. Steven,
observing one of Danny's fingers hovering over the crumpled tabloid
newspaper beside his plate, leaned forward. 'Now there's a story for
you. There's a man who shows you what can be done with a wee bit
of the old people magic.' He slapped his hand down on the plastic
table, loudly and flatly, as if he were killing a fish.

'See, that's what youse people lack, at the end of the day, know
what I'm saying? The common touch. That's what you need. The
power of the masses. The ability to get people to dance to your
tune.'

The cafe was depressingly familiar to Steven. All the tables had
plastic tops surrounded by a cracked rim; the chairs were low and
squat with the kind of seats that clung to your trousers if you sat
in them for too long. It was full of people like Danny. In his head
he might be a philosopher of staggering reach and vision, but to the
wider world he was just another wee fat guy from Glasgow. That
was all he was, and all he ever would be.

'Look at this guy', said Danny. Steven looked at the upturned
picture of Saint Sebastian and wrung another measure of contempt
from his nose. A 14th-century nonentity, shot into the public spotlight

by the Vatican's vulgar campaign to turn the canonisation progress
into a crude X Factor-style publicity contest. And now, because of
some spurious Glasgow connection, his candidacy for sainthood had
been blessed with the official backing of Danny's favoured tabloid.
'Vote Sebastian, Glasgow's adopted saint, for Sanctus '09', it
proclaimed. Judging from his turnip-shaped head and outsized
torso, old Seb would certainly fit in among the regular clientele in
here, Steven thought.

Danny held his breath and squeezed another gloop of ketchup
onto his plate. He reached inside his jacket in a grotesquely elaborate
manoeuvre and drew out a grimy, plastic-covered book entitled
Sebastian: the Life of an Everyday Miracle Worker. 'Here', he said,
laying it on the table. 'There's your man right there. Take that
home and inwardly digest it.'

*

Like all his best ideas, the one for the time compass had come
to Danny in a flush of adrenaline laced with whisky. The exact
sequence of events had become hazy in his memory: he had spent
the afternoon in the library, reading a book on the discovery of
longitude and the world-expanding clocks of John Harrison. That
night, as he mulled over a double dose of Stewart's Cream of the
Barley, the theories and knowledge slowly blended in the pot still of
his mind, fired by a thick shot of moonshine philosophy. Time was
not straight, but curved, Einstein had told him. It could be moulded
and twisted.

He clung to the thought like a captain lashed to the ship's wheel
in a heavy storm. The reason people couldn't travel in time was
because they didn't have a map. Before Harrison's day, the oceans
were the ends of the earth because people didn't know how to navigate
them.

The blast of inspiration shook him sober. What was more, he
could get all the parts he needed at his local DIY store. Just like
that guy he'd read about once who made a satellite dish out of a
dustbin lid. If he could do it, why not Danny? He fumbled in a
drawer for a notebook, scribbled down the names of all the parts he
needed, took another nip of whisky and passed out in an ecstasy of
delirium.

The next day he bought the parts he needed from the DIY store and assembled them, aided in his toil by four cans of beer. The finished contraption was solid black, about the size of a briefcase, and garnished with two dials fashioned from combination locks. Danny's heart was pulping. He knew it ought to work, but reality was rougher round the edges than theory. He turned one of the dials a tiny fraction, clung on to the machine, closed his eyes tightly and pressed the button.

When he opened his eyes again, he was still in his kitchen. He was on the point of swearing out loud, but then he noticed that the dark corner by the fridge wasn't quite as dark, and that there were only three crushed cans lying beside his work bench. He went to the fridge, feeling his steps laden down with history like those Neil Armstrong took on the moon. And sure enough, when he opened the door, there was the virgin beer can with its ring-pull unviolated. Danny danced something like a jig, or the closest thing his corpulent body would allow, ripped open the beer can and downed its contents in one gulp.

*

Steven came back to the table with a second round of coffee. It had the almost acid aroma that distinguished cafes in court canteens all over the country. 'Looks like it might be a while before we get called,' he said. 'Want to nip out for a cigarette?'

'No, it's okay, honestly, mate,' Danny said. 'I dinnae go in for that kind of stuff. Bad for your heart, don't you know? Saint Sebastian could have told you that.'

Steven parted his eyebrows in mild exasperation. 'You know, you might want to give a bit less thought to medieval monks and a bit more to what you're going to say to the sheriff. You're potentially in very serious trouble.'

'See, this is the problem, right?' Danny said. 'You're not looking at the bigger picture here. All you can think of is your petty rules about how people should and shouldn't behave, constantly trying to stuff folk into wee boxes, to grind them down until they hardly exist. Five hundred years from now, who's gonnae give a monkey's about your wee insignificant middle-class neuroses?'

Steven spread his fingers on the table. 'I get your point, Danny,

I really do. But we're not five hundred years from now, we're here, about to go into court, and where you're sitting, two charges of theft are anything but a petty concern. Now, I'm happy to sit and talk about Saint Sebastian all afternoon, but just for now can we just nail this point about what you're going to say in your defence? Just for me?'

'All right, then, mate', said Danny, relinquishing. 'But I tell you, that cow in the pharmacy, man, she does ma nut. See in the medieval days, women like that who brewed up potions in the backs of their hooses were burned at the stake as witches. In her case it'd be a fitting punishment.'

'Yes, Danny, but this is the 21st century, and not only will you not be burning her at the stake, you're also not allowed to steal pills from her pharmacy. Do you follow?'

'Aye, on you go, mate', said Danny, swirling a finger over the book cover.

'Good. Now, let's take it from the top. Why did you steal the drugs?'

*

The holy man appeared in Fiesole a dozen more times that year, and each time he brought joy and comfort through his mysterious concoctions. Each time he would be led to the house of a sick child, and there he would silently bring out a tonic and signal instructions for how it should be administered. He never spoke a word, yet though his digits were large and clumsy and he had difficulty manoeuvring his gargantuan body, never once did he fail to communicate his intent.

The people in the town grew ever more curious about this benevolent stranger. They wanted to know, most of all, where he had come from. One day a scholar arrived in Fiesole, having heard rumours of the miracles being worked in the town, and bearing a map of the world as they knew it, stretching all the way out to the sea at Pisa. Through gestures they made plain to the stranger that they desired to know his place of origin, and invited him to mark the spot with a stone. But instead the man asked for a piece of charcoal and began to draw on the far left-hand side of the map. The people were aghast, for what he drew at first resembled the face of a witch, with a long, drooping nose off to one side and a deep scar of a mouth. But when he flattened off the tip of the hat and drew little chains of beads above them and to the side, they understood that this must be the shape of his country. Finally he marked a dot, roughly where the witch's epiglottis would have been, and indicated that this was the place he had ventured from. The people looked at each other, awestruck and disquieted. Then the scholar took the map away and rode off. And the mysterious healing man rose and departed for the last time.

*

Danny offered no explanation to the Sheriff Court for why he stole from the pharmacy, but insisted the drugs were not for himself. The court ruled that he must have been involved in dealing on some level, but in the absence of hard evidence imposed a two-year jail sentence. When not in his cell, Danny spent most of his time in the prison library. In the same edition of the newspaper that reported on his case, under the headline Phantom Pharmacy Raider Named and Shamed, he read that Saint Sebastian had won the public vote for canonisation. For the first time in his life, Danny felt fulfilled.

Gordon Darroch was born in Norwich, educated in Edinburgh and now lives in Glasgow. He has been a journalist for The Herald and the Press Association and is now working freelance. When not wrestling with his own or other people's words, he can often be found running around his home in big circles. Occasionally he plays the cello. His website is at gordondarroch.wordpress.com

No Time

By Karl Henry

The clock, it ticks on the wall. Ticks past the time. Constant and everlasting, ticking away until that day. The day that everything will change. The day the world will lose its self and the people will follow in its wake. The day time will stop passing and in its place the people will tick away one by one, second by second. The day when we will stop losing time and all that will be left is life. Tick... Tick... Tick... that day has come.

It started unlike any other day. The sun didn't rise. The birds didn't sing. My alarm clock didn't sound. But that was least of my worries. My day when time didn't pass was going to be the longest of my life.

I don't know why I'm writing this. I don't know if anyone other than me is ever going to read it. I don't know if anyone is going to survive. It's been 23 hours, 51 minutes and 58 seconds since time stopped. So far, as close as my maths can make it 4,764,967,064 billion people are dead, and at any second I could join that figure.

No time, that's what the news was calling it. The amount of

time that has passed since time stopped. Before the news stopped broadcasting there was a scientist, who had a theory. He thought that the mass of people dying was because time had stopped. His theory was that 77,892 people were dying a second and if you multiplied that number by 86,400 the number of seconds in a single day, you would get the world's population. I believe him but that doesn't matter now. Nothing does. Nothing I do makes a difference. All that's left for me is to wait. Wait for my second.

I'm not sad or upset in any way at the thought of my death. That's only because I now understand that all I can do is wait. The people still living have no choice. I know this because four hours, 16 minutes and 33 seconds ago I tried to take my own life. The only choice I thought I had left. I was wrong.

In my bedroom, in a small wooden chest at the bottom of my wardrobe, is a gun. Don't ask me why I have a gun; you'll not have the chance. I can't say for sure if everyone will be able to understand what it is like to hold a gun to your head and pull the trigger. I can. I'm unsure if everyone else will be able to imagine this. I can, I was in that situation.

Imagine how hard it is to lift that gun. Feel the weight of it in your left hand. The cold steel sending a slight shiver up your spine. You can feel the weight of the bullet in your other hand, notice how light it feels in comparison as you load it in to the gun. You take a moment or two, maybe even three, as you come to terms with what it is you are about to do. As you raise the gun to your head, taking that last slow breath as you close your eyes and pull the trigger. Now imagine what it's like when the gun doesn't fire. When the gun can't fire. The thought of having to lift that gun again is un-imaginable. I was able to lift that gun again. I was able to hold it to my head; and I was able to pull the trigger. The gun still didn't fire.

I don't know if this is true, but, like the scientist on TV, I have a theory. I don't think we're allowed to die until it's our second. I have never been a religious person. Never believed in a higher power. Today that has changed. It's the only way that any of this can make sense in my head. There must be a higher power. A higher power that stopped time 23 hours, 54 minutes and 26 seconds ago. A higher power that has given each of us a second. I believe this because my gun works. There is a hole in my wall that proves it.

We all take time for granted. We never think about how much time we have left. When we are going to die. I can't help but find it ironic. Ironic that it takes time to stop before anyone notices how much we have left. Now it's all anyone can think about. I haven't made up my mind yet. Whether or not I'm one of the lucky few whose second was left near the end. I feel as if I've entered a state of enlightenment. I now realise the important things that matter. The things that if I had another day of time, I would do. I would tell my wife that I loved her more often. I would buy my daughter the Elmo toy she has wanted all week. I would finally tell my parents that when I was 20 I took a year out of university and bummed around. I would do the things that any one of us would do if we had more time. Then I would do more again.

My name is Conrad Gray. I am 43 years old. I worked at K.J.H investments. I loved my family. At some point in the next four minutes and 44 seconds, my second will arrive. I can only hope that there will be someone alive to read this. Someone who wasn't given a second. Someone that surv

Karl Henry is in early twenties and is from the small town of Kilrea in Northern Ireland. He came to Dundee in the summer of 2006 to study Web Site Development, but discovered that it wasn't for him. Upon this realisation he decided to study English. He has completed the Professional Writing Skills course at Dundee College and will begin studying English and Film Studies at Dundee University in September. In his spare time Karl enjoys making short films, which he writes and stars in. Karl hopes one day to be a successful screen writer.

Road to Heaven
By Amy Kinmond

If someone told me death was gonna be so damn boring, I would've been more careful. Yes I was speeding, but I was gonna miss Roxie's play. I'd told Frank at the studio I wouldn't miss it, but still he had to do another scene. Anyway, don't blame me; blame the guy who gave a license to that idiot that didn't look before entering the highway.

Hi, Adam Payne here. You're wondering where you know me from? I'll give you a hint, imagine a scar running up this side of my face. Yep, you've guessed it; you're speaking to the world famous Adam Payne, from the 'Terminal Vengeance' movies. Sure, I've done other stuff; I nailed the part of Iago when touring with 'Othello', and had every person in the theater crying when I played John Merrick in the remake of 'The Elephant Man'. Although, I must admit, people always see an action star – a damn good one, at that.

Anyway, story of my death? I would've thought my life to be more important, but doesn't matter; it feels like I've been dead longer than alive.

Yeah, so I got out my car to find I wasn't even on the highway
anymore. There was a road, but it wasn't the same. I knew I was
dead straight away, I mean come on - it was pretty obvious. For
one, I left the four-car pileup without a scratch. For another, everything seemed kinda blurred. It wasn't my eyes - had 20/20 vision
all my life and I don't see why that would be any different in the
afterlife. No, I could see the highway fine, but as soon as I looked
off the road – well it was blurry.

The crash scene wasn't there anymore, just my Mustang, still
untainted. Thank God, I would have died if anything happened to
her. Mind the pun. The sun was high in the sky, beaming down
on the road. Traffic was jammed to the horizon, and someone had
already hit their horn, so I told them where they could stick their
horn, and stepped back into my car.

I tried to start the car but couldn't. I didn't get it; I went to the
hood and she was looking like a dream. But she just wouldn't turn
over. Just like a woman. Had no choice but to leave her behind.
Knew she'd understand.

I went to the edge of the road, making sure I didn't step off
into the hazy side – I doubted it was solid. As a matter of fact, if I
squinted it looked like the road was above land. I was sure I could
see something moving in the blur, something distant. Don't know
why, but part of me knew it was cars on the old highway, going
along without me. I wondered where Sara and Roxie were. Did they
know yet? Or was Sara just pissed at me missing the play? Suppose
it didn't matter, they'd have to get on without me.

I walked alongside the traffic for a while, the unblurry traffic:
could have been ten minutes, could have been three hours. What
with the jam I was actually better off walking anyway, the sun was
warm on my back, and after all, what was the hurry? I was dead.

Eventually the jam let up, with no trace of the cause. The sun
still hadn't dropped from its peak so I just kept on walking, but I
didn't know where I was going.

The strange thing about the highway was that it wasn't all that
strange. Same grey tarmac. Same dull people racing along it as
if they couldn't wait to get where they're going. And where were
they going? I could only guess it was to the afterlife. Heaven, hell,

whatever. I noticed that there were no laneways, or off ramps, it
was just one long road with an endless destination.

Suddenly it got dark. No dusk, no dawn, one moment the sun
was high, the next the moon had taken the limelight. Another
thing, it was always either full or absent. Everything was black and
white in this damn world.

Anyway, when it got dark it also became cold. So cold it felt as
though a layer of ice would crystallize on my skin. I knew I had to
get out of this, so I stuck my thumb out and waited for a hitch.

Most cars just passed me by. What's with that? It's not like I
would end up raping or murdering them, I mean, we're dead. But
I guess people get stuck in their old ways. Eventually one person
stopped and pulled down their window. It was a real dump of a car,
a beat-up Camero, but not what you'd call vintage; paint was flaking
off it, and the stuffing was falling out the seats. Still, beggars, huh?

Once the window was down I asked him politely for a lift. Okay I
may have used the phrase 'white trash', but I mean, driving around
like that he should be used to it.

Well somehow he took offence, I tell you, some people just can't
handle constructive criticism. He mumbled something about different
paths, and being 'born alone' and 'dying alone', then drove off in
a hurry, leaving me in the cold. Just what I needed, some lunatic
muttering riddles at me.

I decided not to try to hitch again, perhaps it was pride, but it
also took so damn long to get one car to stop, it would be morning
before I got another. Plus, I was shivering like crazy, hoping to God
I'd reach wherever I was going soon.

I'd been walking along the highway for some time, I spotted a little girl sitting on the side of the road, her arms wrapped around her
knees. Now I should probably say, I wasn't the only one walking, I
would occasionally pass people at the side, but they never looked the
type you'd want to engage in conversation with – they're wondering
whether to stab you or worship you as the next Messiah. Fucking
weirdoes.

I looked at this girl and her brown curls, and I saw my own little
Roxie. I couldn't believe, even in death, this girl would be expected
to fend for herself in a place like this.

I sat down next to her, afraid of frightening her and handed her
my coat. Why she couldn't have died wearing a thick woolly jumper,
instead of a thin summer t-shirt? But hey, what could I do – I'm
soft at heart.

She took it with all the caution of a timid animal. If death treated
children like this, I wished to God I was still alive to protect my
daughter.

She was wary of me at first, of course. Didn't recognize me from
the TV – I tell you, some people are so uneducated, but she was
only young so I forgave her. I told her about my girl, who was
probably about the same age. She didn't look up, but her ears
pricked up slightly at my voice. I occasionally asked her questions,
moving on casually if she didn't answer until she finally began to
talk. She got used to me, and told me how she missed her Mom, but
she knew her Granny was here somewhere.

It was still as cold as hell and without my jacket I was beginning
to wonder if I was going to freeze to death, or to life, or whatever.
I told her we had to keep moving, but she began to cry, wanting
her Mom. I explained to her that at the end was heaven where
her Gran would be, and she could watch after her Mom, blah blah
blah. All that crap. All the time thinking, is this really my job?
Shouldn't there be someone waiting for her? Or was heaven short
staffed or something?

Eventually she came with me, but she tired so quickly I put her
on my shoulders. Good thing I worked out when I was alive, otherwise
we both would have been screwed.

Soon after the sun appeared, she jumped off my shoulders. I
didn't get why, but she said she was there, that her journey was
over, and then she stepped off the highway into the haze and just
disappeared. I blinked and she was gone. And you know I still
kinda miss her.

I walked for a while deep in thought. I realized this must have
been why the cars had been tailing off, why I'd seen fewer and
fewer people. Everyone had their own paths, or at least, that's what
I figured. I reckoned some paths would veer off into other religions,
but what about that girl? She talked about Jesus and that, so I
assumed she was a Christian like me. Or perhaps I was the one

that wasn't Christian? Perhaps I didn't count? I wasn't a big fan of the whole going to church thing. Hell when I was young, I took the money my parents gave me for the collection, and got an ice cream at the beach with my mate. I was never really into the praying thing either. In truth, religion hadn't really played a part in my life – but did that mean I had to suffer in death?

Soon after, the highway ground to a halt, the tarmac was replaced by a muddy path with the occasional car abandoned at the side of the road. I'd stepped into a desolate country landscape, hell, more of a jungle. Trees flooded the side of the path so thick that it was a miracle light managed to filter its way through the leaves. I started to quicken my pace, breaking into a slight jog as I could taste the end, and I sure as hell wasn't going to face another night in this place. I'm pretty good at jogging, used to go out every morning; so once I started, I quickly began passing people, but didn't engage. One guy tried to stop me to ask about where we were, but I made like I didn't hear him. I knew where I was going and no-one was getting in my way.

Thanks to my morning jogs, I was able to keep up this fast pace for a long time, until something stopped me in my tracks. The scenery wasn't changing much; in fact, part of me even thought I was on some kind of proverbial treadmill, until I saw it. A fork in the road.

For the first time in my journey I was faced with a choice. At the fork the landscape began to grow rockier with the left side sloping upwards and the right showing a gentle descent down. I turned to start heading up the left side but stopped suddenly. It was too easy. Up to heaven, down to hell, there is no way it would be that simple. But I couldn't head down, could I? That would be asking for trouble.

The great thinker that I am, I just sat at the side and waited for someone to pass. It wasn't long before some traveler sauntered along. I realized he was the guy that tried to ask me something earlier. I took a deep breath and stood up, sticking my hand out and flashing him the award-winning smile that bought me the lead in 'Something like Love'.

'Hi, Adam Payne.'

'I know who you are, you're the guy who ran right past me when I was asking for help,' he said.

'Yeah, sorry about that,' I continued smoothly. 'I had to run to meet you here. You see, right before you reach the otherworld you get interviewed by your favorite celebrity, yours truly. Any questions?'

'Yeah, my favorite celebrity? Where's Michael Garcia? That guy's awesome.'

Ouch. The guy just didn't know taste. Sure Garcia could get a few cheap laughs, but I always felt the part. I had the audience in the palm of my hand; Garcia was just a poser.

I continued regardless, 'No, see you think you like Garcia, but your subconscious says different. Anyway, first question, just a simple one to start off with, get you in the flow, what do you see in front of you?'

Cheeky bastard quirked an eyebrow at me, 'What? Behind the has-been actor? I see the forest turning into mountain land.'

'And that land is going up? Is there only one path?'

'Yeah, look man, just turn round and see for yourself.'

Great, so now I knew the fork was unique to me, just like the path that little girl went up was unique to her. I began to press him with questions. Most fun I'd had since I died, reminded me of my days in 'Legal Justice', before Hollywood found me and I left TV behind. When I played a lawyer who had to delicately pry apart the trash and lies, to find the glittering diamond of the truth underneath.

I won't bore you with the details. God, this man loved to talk; he was the most self-centered, narcissistic and arrogant person I had ever met. And I worked in Hollywood. But I did learn that he had done time in prison for robbery when he was short on cash. He tried to make out like he had no choice. Jesus, just get a job like everyone else. Afterwards he trotted up the left side of the fork, leaving me waiting for the next person. Well you didn't think I was going to base my entire fate on some snobby prick, did you? The rule for good investigation is to always check your facts, hey a criminal like that was probably going to hell, but you never know. Isn't God meant to be about forgiveness and all that crap?

The next person I saw was a girl in her twenties. Gorgeous and so excited to see a celebrity like me – I had to tell her from the start that I was happily married so she would back off. A pang hit me when I thought how long it could be until I saw Sara again. But

I pushed it aside and kept questioning her.

Much more interesting than the first guy, friendly too, and she clearly had taste in movies. She had spent her teens doing volunteer work, had stayed celibate until marriage (amazing what people tell good-looking celebrities) and except for one joint in College she seemed to have a clean track record.

But then she headed off, veering up the side of the mountain in the same direction as the criminal.

That threw a spanner in the works. I'd have to stay there until night broke and interview every passerby, then I had a stroke of genius. I wasn't a big reader of the Bible but I remembered the Ten Commandments, and I was pretty sure they were law. Problem was it'd been since Sunday school days since I'd read them. I was pretty certain that 'Thou Shalt Not Kill' was a rule, but it wasn't likely any serial killers would turn up in this short space of time. I didn't have all day. The only other one I remembered was 'Honor Thy Mother and Father', just because it seemed so ridiculous. Nothing wrong with honoring the parents, it's just a bit trivial beside something like 'Don't kill'.

I thought of that Ass I interviewed first. Was stealing in the Commandments? I wasn't sure, so I just stuck with the whole mother and father thing. At least if I found someone who happened to kill their parents I'd know they were definitely going to hell.

Before nightfall five more people passed me. I got an ex-heroin addict who was kicked out her home by disappointed parents (down); an army veteran who had killed for his country (down); a firefighter who had lost his leg saving a family (up); a scientist who did what her parents wanted (down); and an ex-alcoholic who had turned his life around and now tried to help others like him (up).

Night fell, the cold came and at this point I didn't care about eternity, I just needed out the damn cold. A fiery hell was beginning to sound pretty good by then.

It all seemed so random, I mean the junkie going to the same place as the national hero? The thief to the same place as the firefighter? What kind of coin-toss God was this? And the scientist and the heroin addict put a stop to my 'honor Mom and Dad' theory. The only conclusion I came to was that people lie. Even with my capable interrogation skills, I could not get to the core of their life story. Even if they didn't lie, maybe people are just too damn complicated, maybe no one can be summed up in a nutshell.

In the end I had to throw all my logic away. The cold was ripping at my skin and a decision had to be made. I thought of Sara, and of Roxie. I knew I couldn't be with them yet, and God I hope they don't join me too soon. Even if I wouldn't be able to see them, I wanted to be as close to them as I possibly could be. I headed down.

Amy is an enthusiastic new writer who hopes to, one day, become an enthusiastic old writer. She has had a couple of pieces published and is currently in third year studying English Literature at the University of Dundee. She hopes you enjoyed her story.

Oblivious Fish
By Corinna Weyreter

It was another beautiful day. There'd been many of them lately and Fin was in no doubt that summer had started. Every morning light began to creep tentatively through the water, gradually gathering momentum until it burst into even the deepest corners of the lake. It brought with it a warmth that was transforming the sparse, dormant vegetation of winter into towering forests of luxuriant green. Long velvet leaves quivered in the gentle currents, casting shadows that rippled against the brightness. Within this fresh, ever-changing scenery Fin found adventure with his best friend Scales. Life was good.

Together they explored far and wide, fearing no place and no creature. They often swam near the surface, poking their dorsal fins or the tops of their tails out into the cool void, but they knew the world stopped beyond the lake, that life wasn't possible without water. It was youth that propelled them to live on the edge sometimes.

'I'm hungry,' Scales announced, as they cruised along side by side. 'Let's go over to that reed forest, there are bound to be minnows hiding in there,' and without waiting for an answer he swam away, Fin following contentedly in his wake.

Scales was right about the minnows. The friends immediately went into pursuit, forcing the school of small fish to shoot between the gently swaying reeds, chasing it one way and then the other. They worked as a team, enjoying the hunt, thrilled by their dominance. With ease they isolated the weakest, taking turns to pick them off one by one. Before long, Fin had eaten enough, but his friend wasn't satisfied.

'Look over there,' Scales said, catching his breath. 'A juicy, fat little fish all alone. It won't even see me coming,' and he shot off towards the shimmering prey.

Fin hung back and watched his friend fondly, happy as ever to be his shadow.

And then, without warning, the water erupted in the distance.

Suddenly Scales disappeared inside a turbulent swirl of bubbles that moved steadily towards the lake's edge. Fin raced over to make sure he was all right, but there was no sign of him or his fat little quarry. Fin's frantic calls drifted away unanswered, his heart pounded to an unfamiliar beat of fear. Terrified, he followed the bubbling trail, driven on by desperation and love.

But all he found was the edge of the world.

Back and forth he swam, weaving between plants, searching every possible nook, but his friend remained elusive. Scales had simply vanished.

Too soon darkness seeped through the lake like black ink, cooling the water as it spread. Fin knew he had to find a safe place to sleep, and he was afraid to stay by the reeds. With an aching heart he swam away from his friend, away from the place where he had lost him. He knew that he would never see Scales again.

*

This is the life, Joe thought, as he sat fishing by the lake. A lazy summer, just like those he'd loved as a boy. After a lifetime of hard work he'd come full circle. On Friday he had walked out of the office for the last time and driven straight to the cabin to start his retirement.

He hadn't caught anything today, and he reeled in the latest lure to swap it for a fat little silver one. He was sure it would prove irresistible in such glorious sunshine.

He cast off and the line jerked almost immediately. He pulled the rod up sharply to make sure this one stayed on the hook. It was strong and not about to surrender without a fight. Joe held the rod firmly and quickly reeled in the line.

Then all of a sudden he had it, a beautiful trout that glistened in the sunlight as it landed on the grass by his feet. He tried not to look at the eyes as it curved itself desperately one way and then the other in search of water and escape. Joe knew the eyes couldn't focus in air, but still it seemed to him that there was always a flash of terror, when for one diabolical second the fish realized that there was a world beyond the water, one in which it couldn't swim or breathe, one in which fish-eating monsters lived.

He got his knife and thrust it into the top of the trout's head, piercing the brain. There was a shudder and then the look he hated disappeared.

'Oh, what a beautiful fish,' Joe's wife Mary said, as he walked up the stairs to the cabin's veranda.

'Trout,' he grinned, holding it up proudly. 'It'll be wonderful for dinner.'

While Joe did the cleaning and gutting, Mary prepared the vegetables. They were a team, had been for forty years. Some of their friends had got divorced, some had learnt to put up with each other, but she and Joe were genuinely happy. Mary tried not to think about it, fearing fate would be tempted to dole out a bout of bad luck and bring their perfect world crashing down around them. She was not religious, but she was fanatically superstitious.

'It's such a lovely evening I'll grill it on the barbecue,' Joe said.

'Good idea. I'll put the potatoes on the boil.'

'Why don't you get that Chardonnay from the fridge? It'll go perfectly with the fish.'

And so Mary toasted Joe for catching the trout, and Joe toasted the trout for its sacrifice. They watched the sun melt into the horizon and savoured the aroma drifting from the barbecue on the warm summer breeze. Life was good.

'Oh, this is delicious,' Mary said, taking a bite of the tender fish.

'If I can keep catching these we'll eat like kings,' Joe said, smiling.

And then, without warning, he dropped his cutlery and grabbed his throat with both hands.

He staggered to his feet and stared at Mary with wide, shocked eyes, his face a terrifying shade of red. He was choking.

She jumped up, her chair falling over as she rushed across to Joe.

'Oh God, oh God,' she cried; there was no god of superstition for her to call upon now. She thumped her husband on the back, cautiously at first, violently when his hands stayed clamped around his neck. She began to panic, her blows falling haphazardly, ineffectually. Joe fell to his knees. His face was turning purple.

Mary's mind raced too quickly to think clearly. She remembered something about a manoeuvre, but she didn't know what to do, she'd never taken a first aid course in her life. Tears blurred her vision and she wiped them away roughly. She had to make him cough up the obstruction.

Kneeling down behind Joe she reached her arms around his middle, but he was so large she had to stretch. The potbelly she found so cuddly in bed was now preventing her from saving his life. With great effort she clasped her right hand with her left and jerked upwards. But it was hopeless; she had no strength, no power. This was what it meant to be powerless. She tried again and again, but her attempts were little more than desperate squeezes.

She could not save him.

She felt the weight of his body sink onto her hands a second before his arms dropped by his sides.

*

Deius was taking care of deliveries from Earth this evening and it was a busy shift. Souls had been pouring in from every corner of that planet and he was running around like a devil with its tail on fire getting them all processed and packed into the right boxes. A few new wars had sprung up on Earth, so more souls from the warring regions were arriving these days, but otherwise there were the usual quotas of old age, heart failures, diseases, and traffic accidents. The population of that small planet was shooting up every year and it was now one of their most productive suppliers, nearly one hundred and fifty thousand deliveries every single day. Deius

hadn't been feeling his best lately and would have preferred being
assigned to a quieter planet, but you got what you were given, there
was no complaining here.

The white light flashed again. Another soul emerged into the
brightness from the black tunnel and dropped onto the conveyer
belt. It was a short white fat one this time, no hair and a livid
purple head. Joe Walters, sixty-five, American, choked on a fish
bone the information said. Its eyes were still open; Deius hated it
when they arrived like that. He knew the eyes couldn't focus without
air, but still it seemed to him that there was always a flash of
terror when for one diabolical second the human soul realized that
there was a world beyond planet Earth, one in which it couldn't
move or breathe, one in which soul-eating monsters lived.

Deius picked up the new arrival and placed it in the box labelled:
Earth, Anglo-Saxon, Male, Mild. He closed the lid and the look he
hated disappeared.

Working hard all night had made Deius hungry, but not for
Earth souls, he'd seen too many of those tonight. He stopped off at
the delicatessen on his way home and bought a large box of mixed
souls, half a dozen from each of his four favourite universes. He
asked for a very hot mixture even though he knew he shouldn't.
He'd eaten a lot of those recently and reacted badly to them, but it
was like an addiction. The mild ones just didn't satisfy him anymore,
they didn't give him the buzz he needed to get through the day.
Mild souls had led such mundane existences, whereas hot souls sizzled
with the spice of life.

Back home Deius sat on his balcony and gazed out at the
interconnecting universes. He never got tired of the beauty of the
megaverse. He opened the box and looked at the twenty-four delicacies
arranged so tantalizingly in the compartments. He took his time
selecting the first one, but after he'd slurped it down he quickly
picked another, and then another, gorging himself. They were all
fresh, raw, exactly the way he liked them. They tasted delicious, but
God they were hot. He knew he should stop eating them but he just
couldn't. He needed to consume every aspect of their lives, devour
all their loves and hates, their jealousies and fears. He craved the
most emotional ones, the ones who had experienced life to the limit;

he wanted to fill himself up with that passion.

Once the last soul had slid into Deius, he stretched out on his back to let them settle. His insides were burning; he knew he'd gone too far this time. He had overdosed. Perhaps this was what he'd wanted all along. He closed his eyes, aware that there was nothing he could do to stop what was on its way.

His life began to fold in on itself, the megaverse was falling down around him, crushing him, forcing him into a tiny space, infinitesimal, self-contained, confined, unique, an essential part of the whole, a jewel within a jewel. Beautiful. He would be oblivious but not realize it, he would be blind but think he could see, he would be alive but not appreciate it. He would be a fish in a lake, he would be a human being on a planet in a universe, and he would still be himself, a deity in the megaverse.

Corinna Weyreter was born in Surrey, England. After graduating in astrophysics from the University of Birmingham she joined the oil company Shell. She worked as a petrophysicist in Scotland, the Netherlands, Oman, Norway and the USA for fifteen years before resigning to sail around the world with her boyfriend. Her book about their adventure will be published later this year. She won first prize in the 1998 Bridport Prize short story competition and since then has had several short stories published. She currently lives in Kuwait, where she writes full time.

To Kill **or** not to Kill?
By Siân Roberts

To kill or not to kill; that is the question. Would my eternal Karma suffer from an affirmative choice, or would the sin tarnish my eternal soul so it wallowed in never ending purgatory? To decline would I gain Karmic points; gain an outline of a halo? Would birds and beasts come sit on my shoulders like St. Francis of Assisi, or would they flee in terror as if I were Satan abroad this mortal plane?

I stood transfixed by the scene before me: the victim lay pinned into a corner, limbs scrambling against the walls. I loomed over them; a shadow blocking out the sun. I could almost feel the terror emanating from the prone figure that lay before me.

I sighed. I could not bring myself to end this life; who knew what else it may achieve? Just because I was afraid did not mean I had the right to kill.

I reached over and slipped a piece of paper under the spider's body. Holding it carefully I moved to the open window and freedom.

Siân Roberts came to Scotland to go to University, fell in love with the country and stayed. She has been living in Dundee for the last five years. Siân writes for relaxation as she is currently at home looking after her twin girls. She attends the Finmill Creative Writing Group.

Keeping the Faithful

By James A. Stewart

D r. McKenzie watched as Father Muir delivered an unsurpassed sermon. McKenzie marvelled at how the priest kept his congregation enraptured; the light inflections, the well timed passion and the mirthful anecdotes all combined to give a performance equal of many a Hollywood star.

The parishioners loved Muir. He was a breath of fresh air in this Glasgow diocese. Whilst Scotland never suffered the same scale of revulsion and indignation as many other Catholic communities, the faith of the flock floundered as credit crunches, wars and political scandal threatened to tear apart the fabric of society in the early twenty-first century.

After Mass, Muir shook hands with many of his followers, rubbed the heads of kids playfully and charmed faithful wives with his humorous banter and encyclopaedic memory. He knew the names and faces of almost everyone in the parish. He could relate to them on so many levels it was as if he was able to change tact and align his personality to whomever he was engaging with. Which, thanks to Juetten's pioneering work on artificial humanoids, he could.

Once the priest had finished with the post-Mass meet and greet, Dr. McKenzie beckoned him to join her at the front row. He locked the door and headed down the length of the church to sit next to her.

'Hello, Father.'

'To what do I owe the pleasure, Lynne?'

'It's a business call, Father, not a social one.'

'I see.' replied the priest.

*

Dr. McKenzie looked over Father Muir. He was nigh-on perfect, a Mk. III model. His predecessors had carried some unfortunate maladies. The Mk. II model was good but the memory core was limited
and, as such, memories crossed over after five to seven years of service. It was not unusual to see a Mk. II priest asking after a long dead relative or to witness him getting confused to see a six or seven year old child in a family when his memory banks throw back images of what was, to the priest, a recent christening.

The memory of the Mk. II priests could be wiped and reformatted, but of course, they couldn't serve the same community. Some intrepid journalists did spot a trend amongst the priest community and questioned whether the teachings of the seminary brought on dementia. The Vatican dealt with these intrusions in its business in the usual manner: a mixture of spin and some direct influencing with the journalists involved. The papal institution made enough noise to counteract the claims of dementia that people got bored and moved on to the latest celebrity break-up.

'Father, you have been in the same diocese for fifteen years now, and whilst some tweaks have been made to sustain the pretence you are ageing, we need to move you. You have been selected for a missionary role in Latin America. I'll upload the Spanish language program to you just now.' Dr. McKenzie placed a small microchip in a flap behind the priest's left ear lobe and ordered the robot to reboot in order to pick up the changes. Ten seconds later, Father Muir was back online.

'I'd like to stay, Lynne.' He was looking the doctor straight in the

eyes. She had carried out an under-the-radar upgrade on Father
Muir two years ago. Her partner, Dr. Nico Juetten, had developed
a program to humanise the emotions the robot priests felt. The
Vatican had kicked it out right away; it wanted nothing other than
covert flocks. The requirements of Pope Mtsuingi, the Vatican's first
African leader, were simple; he wanted a team of robot priests to go
into areas where faith was on the wane and to drum up business.
Nico used to tell Lynne that religion was the second oldest profession
in the world, after prostitution. The Pope had no desire to put any
foibles in his clergy, and thus the doctors and their team of developers
were under strict orders to create a team of priests who would be
personable, engaging, but most of all, obedient

'Lawrence, we went through this last year. You need to move on.'

'I have friends here.' he said.

'I know. But regardless, the time has come. I have brought your
replacement with me. His name is Father O'Connell. He is a mark
three model, formerly known as Father Espinoza. You will swap
places with him and head off to Peru tomorrow.'

Father Muir held Lynne's hand. He was showing genuine sadness
and attachment. These reactions were not in the original design
and whilst the priest was going through an emotional roller-coaster,
Dr. McKenzie couldn't wait to call her partner and tell him of this
development.

'Lynne, please don't send me away. I'll do anything you want.'

'I am sorry, Lawrence, but you know the rules, and we've already
stretched your tenure in this parish out a couple of extra years.'

'My congregation will miss me.'

'Indeed they will. I watched you today and was very impressed.
But Father Espinoza is a worthy replacement. I want you to
complete a handover this evening and we'll leave for the airport
first thing tomorrow. No arguments.'

'No arguments,' was the priest's only reply.

Dr. McKenzie brought Father O'Connell into the church. He was
waiting in her car in standby mode. She activated his program and
the former Spanish speaking Father Espinoza became a genial
Irishman with an affable charm and a love of horses and Gaelic
sports. She took the new parish priest into meet Father Muir. He

looked resentful.

Father Muir greeted his replacement with cold indifference. This was not protocol. He should have embraced his colleague and took the lead in the handover process. Dr. McKenzie stepped in.

'Father Muir, this is Father O'Connell. He will transfer his handover notes on the parish in Lima where you will be going. I expect you to do the same with your former parish.'

'Former parish seems such a cold term,' said Father Muir.

'Harsh, but true, Lawrence. Please don't make this difficult,' replied Lynne, using reasoning as a test of how much the priest had developed.

'OK, Lynne. Leave it with me.'

'Thank you. Lawrence. After the handover, you will become Father Juan Martin Alonso. You will be the parish priest for a small community in the outskirts of Lima, in Peru. You will not retain any memories of your time here. Is that clear?'

'Unfortunately so. Now you're the one making this harder than it needs to be,' he replied. All the while Father O'Connell watched the exchange with no little confusion, he'd never witnessed a Mk. III priest speaking like this.

'OK, sorry,' said Dr. McKenzie as she instigated the handover program. 'I'll leave you two to get to know each other.'

She then took out her mobile communicator and dialled up her partner. He answered right away, dispensing with the formalities.

'How was Father Muir?' he asked.

'Very interesting, Nico. He has developed an attachment to this parish and showed genuine sadness when I insisted he has to go,' replied Lynne, walking to the back of the church to get out of earshot of the priests.

'Excellent. In Peru he'll experience a much harsher environment, one which should accelerate the development of his emotions and "human" nature, if you'll excuse the phrase. His moral compass will grow much faster in an area of extreme poverty.'

'I've recorded the conversation I had with him and am sending you a copy now,' said Lynne as she punched some buttons on her mobile.

Dr. Nico Juetten was listening to the recorded conversation, interspersing it with approving grunts, when a crash came from the front of the church. Lynne dropped her phone and rushed through the green clothed pews to investigate the source and found Father Muir kneeling above the prone body of Father O'Connell, who had a crucifix impaled into his forehead. The damage from this injury would have been enough to destroy the artificial cortex in the robot's head. The candle holder protruding from his backside would have destroyed the back-up disc also. All robot priests know exactly how they are built to make self-servicing as efficient as possible, and Father Muir had inflicted damage to the two areas which are enough to render his replacement dead, in robot terms, at least.

Dr. McKenzie gasped and Father Muir stood up and grabbed her by the throat.

'Please don't make me go, I don't want to. I'll do anything to stay,' he pleaded once more, but this time his grip on the doctor's throat suggested that the plea was more an order, with a hint of menace.

'I-I-I w-w-ont,' she promised as she grasped for air.

He let go of her throat and kneeled over the prone body of Father O'Connell. 'Thank you, Lynne, your understanding is appreciated. Now I must say confession. You can go now.'

Dr. McKenzie made her way toward the back of the church. Her head was spinning with the implications. Father Muir had developed a moral compass alright, but it didn't mean he had to use it for good. She dared not look back, not even when she heard the murderer speak. She unlocked the front door and could hear the faint beginnings of confession, which sounded as if it came through stifled sobs.

'Bless me Father for I have sinned,' said Father Muir, his face a mixture of grimace and grin.

James A. Stewart hails from the small Lanarkshire village of Croy. He lives with his bonnie wife and bairn and is studying creative writing at Newcastle University part-time as an antidote to working for a bank. He is a member of Cumbernauld's Frontier Writers and you can find out more about his writing at: http://jamesstewart13.wordpress.com

Rome
By Clare Olivia Skelton

The phone rang in my house, shrilling down the hallway. It was an old friend, asking me if I would flat-sit. 'Please come, it's lovely this time of year,' she said. 'Oh, and I'm in Rome. I'll post the keys to you.'

I look out her window into the street below. The tree which grows in the piazza is almost at eye level to the bedroom window; it is as if I could step out and walk across its spreading branches, above the pedestrians below.

I think of England: back home it is turning cooler – the autumn months bringing the first morning chill, school uniforms and muddy leaves.

But here, the air is pleasant and I only wear a cardigan and a scarf looped and hooped around my shoulders. September in Rome is sunny and warm. In summer there are sweaty queues of summer tourists who file into the Vatican, fanning their bodies with their folded maps. They are gone now, along with the students on the Inter-Railing trek who pass through the city in an endless stream, nose to the guidebook, eyes on where next.

Now though, the city is quieter, more settled, restoring its faded glamour. A few tourists remain at the Spanish Steps; I offer to take their photograph, and then I wander on.

The Basilica di San Clemante is in a quiet courtyard. The church is painted bright white and inside it is hushed and shady. Incense is burning in pewters and the ornate gold Mary and Child stare with mixed emotions of compassion and reproach that I am only staying for a fleeting moment. I pass on a message from my friend to one of the nuns she had befriended; she blesses me, chattering in Italian while I nod and smile. Then I am out into the yard, beneath the square of blue September sky.

By now it is the siesta and the city is all mine. I walk empty streets, meeting only a few children running home from school, bags swinging wildly, greeting me with exuberant shouts, and a disdainful cat who ignores me. Behind the closed shutters is the sound of voices, and a radio turned low.

The neighbours of my friend call often – inviting me for midnight wine, bringing me some peaches from the morning market Francesca, a widow who lives across the hallway, delivers a pyrex dish of tender artichokes roasted in lemon and parsley. She says she will only stay for a minute, but hours later we are still sitting around the small, rickety table, empty plates pushed away, talking about husbands lost.

One day I walk up the Gianicolo hill, where parkland rolls down to the city buildings. Up here, the mamas are out pushing their babies in huge, black, solemn prams. They half-smile at me as I admire the small brown faces of their children who observe me sternly. Back in the city I drink strong black coffee in street corner café-bars – the men who work there have moustaches and fingers stained with tobacco. I like the solid sugar lumps wrapped in paper, and the way the barmen look up at my reflection in the mirror when they turn their backs.

The market di Testaccio is held every morning, and I stare at the dishes filled with silver, salted cod pieces in slippery oil; delicate white filled zucchini blossoms; olives stuffed with red pimento; circles of cheese and hanging smoked sausage. There is the speciality of Rome

– ricotta cake made with sugar, lemon and vanilla and studded with dried fruits. A man stands over a huge hot plate, pushing around gnocchi made with sizzling hot yellow butter and nutmeg. I talk to the laughing stallholders and try samples of everything with greasy fingers and lips, and a blue paper napkin.

On the day my friend comes home, I go to the market again as I want some flowers to leave in her apartment. On the way back, with a bouquet under my arm, I pass the Trevi Fountain – and I throw in a coin, a charm to ensure that a visitor will return.

I tell my friend that I am always available.

Clare is in her 4th and final year studying English Literature at Dundee. She has loved studying on the Creative Writing programme, giving her the chance to meet so many interesting people. In the August 2009, she read her poems at Edinburgh Book Festival - a wonderful, scary, crazy and exciting experience. She spends her time trying to write a dissertation, walking by the Tay, baking cakes with her flatmates and drinking tea with friends.

Contagious Diseases

By Belica Antonia Kubareli

The Lieutenant wrote 'perspicacious memory', on a cheap card sold in Plaka where tourists bought souvenirs with their last drachmas. Ellie traced the card's provenance from the stamps. The Lieutenant had sent it to her mother's address in Athens and she forwarded it to Italy. Then the card travelled to France and finally arrived in Leeds. Neither the Lieutenant nor her mother knew her whereabouts. The first was dangerous, the latter too afraid of dangers. She stuck his card on the wall, in memory of the country she was forced to flee from. She re-read his two words, unable to understand how a man so generous in love-making could be such a Sphinx. Under the foreign snow of this foreign country, his card reminded her of the Greek sun, closed shutters, sweaty sheets, coffee mugs, half-eaten fruits, the unhooked phone, laughter and heat in his bedroom.

*

In summer 1968 they dived into love as soon as they met at a common friend's seaside house. Their need had no words until the

third of November 1968: George Papandreou, the 'Elder of Democracy'
died and half a million Athenians flooded the roads attending his
funeral, singing 'When are the skies going to clear?' - A manifes-
tation of hatred against the Colonels. Ellie was in the front line of
the demonstration when she saw him talking on his walkie-talkie,
amongst his regiment. The soldiers waited for his orders to attack
the students. A curt gesture, as if cutting a rock with the side of his
palm and the troops fired. She fled Greece on the fifth of November
with the assistance of the underground resistance movement. The
Lieutenant kept searching for her, asking her mother, begging their
common friends for some explanation. They knew he was a Lieutenant but no-one knew he was allied to the Junta before the funeral,
so they kept their mouths shut. It took the Lieutenant months to
find out she was involved in the underground movement and the
information left him aghast. He was thinking of his career if their
relationship was discovered, and of their common friends who all of
a sudden stopped seeing him. A mixture of embarrassment, fury and
guilt overwhelmed him. He liked these people but what if they were
members of the resistance movement too? For a while he played
with the idea of giving their names to the Secret Police. Logic
prevailed: the investigators would surely love to know how and why
he had such friends.

*

February 1970 he got a promotion worth celebrating. Only he
had no-one to celebrate with. His family had denounced him for
allying with the Colonels. His father called him a 'brain-washed
shithead'; to the Lieutenant, the Junta was a revolution for the sake
of Greece, which had fallen into political chaos. He bought food and
wine from a taverna. The moment he paid the bill, he realised he
had asked for fries with rigani and grated feta, Ellie's favourite. He
tried to restrain himself but as he stepped out of the taverna, the
salty thickness of his tears reached his lips. The taverniaris said to
his waiters: 'It's the first time I see a member of the Junta crying.
May all of these bastards cry soon!' The Lieutenant kept crying all
night long. There was no use denying it anymore; his hunger and
thirst for Ellie were still there. It took him a visit to the taverna to
acknowledge the emotional vacuum he had been feeling ever since

he lost her. The dawn found him writing an endless letter which he
tore to pieces. His military education took control and he composed
himself. Yet he couldn't remember how he came to Plaka, Ellie's
favourite neighbourhood.

'Let's pretend we are tourists and do whatever stupidity we want
to!' she'd tell him, trying to break the surface of his military poise,
although he never wore his uniform with her.

*

He bought the first card he found and wrote 'perspicacious memory'
because she had mentioned this word. Ellie was researching Latin
origins in the English language for her dissertation.

'It's from perspicax, which means to see through, to see clearly, to
be perceptive... Are you perceptive enough to realise I am the love
of your life?' He dropped the card in the post-box, acknowledging that
Ellie was the love of his life and he didn't give a shit about his career,
so long as he could be with her. But it was too late. He gauged his
chances. What if he left the army? Impossible - the Junta would jail
him. What if he fled Greece and searched for her? Impossible – he
was sure her mother didn't know her whereabouts and her friends
wouldn't disclose anything. Besides, they would arrest him at the
airport, or even if he managed to escape, the resistance fighters
would assume he was a mole. He wished Ellie would remember and
understand it was a delayed avowal of his love.

*

When the card reached Ellie, his words meant nothing. Almost
two years on the run had left her no soul for him. He was a Junta
man and she was a Junta fighter. When the cold in her meagre
room became unbearable she slipped the card into her pocket and
took it for a stroll. Since cards do not feel the cold, she didn't feel
it either. She treated the card to hot chocolate at 'Acropolis', a too
expensive Cypriot cafeteria ideal for old British couples who dream
of Greek antiquities which they will never see. She talked with the
manager trying hard to grasp his dialect. A mixture of Greek and
English melancholy penetrated her while listening to him. She was
glad when the Cypriot gave her a fat cheque, 'Gia ton Agona', as he
said. Ellie went to the resistance head-quarters and handed her
leader the cheque. The man congratulated her. 'We shall use this

money for the Alexandros Panagoulis' liberation campaign. Oriana
Fallaci is doing her best but we need more money…' and then in
a fatherly manner, 'What about you? Do you need money, koritsi
mou?'

'No, thank you, I've got a job.'

'That's good. What job?'

'House cleaner …'

The man stared at a loss for words. He knew Ellie and her family. If
her mother learned that her delicate daughter was cleaning houses,
she'd die. 'Courage Ellie, the Colonels won't last forever.'

'Any news from my father?'

'They've moved him from Makronisos to Aegina. He's better
there. better food, fewer rocks to dig up. He is allowed to teach
young prisoners. Honestly…'

Ellie cast him a fleeting smirk. 'I have to go. Buses are rare on
Sundays.'

Another Sunday in exile; another Sunday in this country whose
language doesn't include the word 'xenitia'. Strangeness, expatriotism,
emigration, alienation, or even exile cannot hold xenitia's brutality.
Ellie didn't get the bus, she couldn't return to her room. She fooled
her solitude by wandering around Leeds. The wet cobbles and the
steep slopes of the city streets made her nervous. Used to walking
on the dry Athenian tarmac she was always in fear of slipping
and falling down. Still the area's poverty, the soot brick walls, the
chimneys, the barren back-yards, the constant drizzle resonated
with her. She enjoyed the locals' accent and smiled at the word 'love'
which she heard as 'loaf' at first. A piercing longing for the Sundays
at home, with the families preparing lunch, plagued her: mothers
serving spaghetti with parmesan and braised beef swimming
in tomato sauce, with basil, onion, garlic and a bit of cumin; the
daughters bringing the salad and the wine, the men grating the
parmesan, joking with the boys. If only her family could have a
Sunday gathering again. But her family didn't exist anymore: her
father was imprisoned, one brother hiding in France, the youngest
in Germany, her mother under house arrest.

*

Ellie and the Lieutenant used to meet on Sunday afternoons.

Each Sunday – siesta time for the normal people – these two tested physical identification, always keeping at bay a little something, as if afraid that if they did everything there would be no reason for another date. They liked pretending they had nothing in common but physical contact. As if what they had was only some bodily experience, a rehearsal leading to the play they were meant to stage with someone else. As if the body bears no memory, no mind. But they never had anything more, with anybody else.

Every time the Lieutenant dared repeat any of their games with another woman, he felt ashamed and afraid. Ellie, wiser than him, never copied the original. Xenitia meant being a sexless resistance fighter.

*

Now she sat at a noisy cafeteria counting her money under the table, to make sure it was enough for a salad as well as the coffee. The fading light signalled the return to her miserable room, the endless hours before sleep, before the dawn in that blue ice that couldn't hypnotise reality.

She would curl up in bed dressed in a night gown in case some comrade knocked at her door. She'd stay lying until her ear would go numb on the pillow, waiting for this terrible winter to go, without any dream of homeland, without thinking of this man who needed only her voice to turn him on, whose body was evaporating from lust, unable to remember the taste of his sweat. Xenitia and exile taught her how to deny any kind of memory. The ostracised imposed oblivion on their minds and souls to survive and fight. She was smoking under the duvet, looking at the smoke filling up the meagre room. She knew she'd wake-up with a throbbing headache again and wished she could wake up back in Greece with the smell of the coffee her mother left on her bedside table.

The Lieutenant didn't smoke. Suddenly she remembered his anxiety to air his flat the moment she was getting dressed to leave. She wondered why he did this, since he was begging her to smoke and exhale in his mouth. Next time I meet him I'll smoke a cigar and drench myself with perfume, she thought with childish naivety, remembering how he carried her into the bathroom and washed her like an invalid, the invalid of love. He claimed all changes caused by Eros were traced on her skin and that's why he hated perfumes.

*

Ellie heard a fracture of a faint sound. The sound of paper. The card. It was suffocating in her coat pocket in the closet. She jumped out of the bed and took it out. She put it against her coffee mug, and exhaled her cigarette smoke onto it. The card is made of paper. What is he made of? How long did it take him to buy this stupid card and write these two words? She wrote an endless humane letter. She sealed the envelope and ran to catch the evening post. She returned to her cage in peace. Her letter would travel through many countries before reaching him. The letter travels; he is stuck with the Junta, she thought.

*

A week later, some comrades visited her to discuss their revolutionary line. One of them noticed the card and said it caused him nostalgia. Ellie gave it to him. Spring, in Leeds on the verge, in full bloom in Greece; Ellie was strolling in exile, gaping at the strange foreign spring, with that sour green which turned to brown whenever it snowed. Astonished at this lame foggy sun, she was running after every shard of sunshine, yearning for some real spring. She rode buses towards unfamiliar areas, gathering money for the Agona against the Junta, knowing that this was not her last year in xenitia, cleaning houses, satisfied she had money for rent, food and tobacco. When she wasn't working she'd go and sit at a café, opposite the university campus. She loved watching all these care-free students who flooded the area. She often lulled her tension by imagining she could continue her studies. But the idea of getting a degree under a fake name woke her up to reality. She'd then get a National Express coach and go to the airport pretending she was flying back home.

*

Her letter arrived when summer was scorching Athens. They had met in summer and the Lieutenant took it as an omen. He started hoping she would return. But he wouldn't open the envelope, afraid of the memories. His colleagues took it for a coded message hidden on the stamps and looked up to him with envy and admiration.

The cleaning lady accidentally threw the letter in the rubbish

along with some other papers. He went mad. He rushed to the huge
dustbin in the park, tearing open all the black bags. Eventually he
recovered it. The Lieutenant, who hated dirt, kissed the envelope,
and walked the distance to his flat, enfolding it in his palms as if
it were her body. He rushed into the bedroom and rid himself of
his clothes; Ellie was staring. She came all demanding, all giving,
in that empty dirty bed. The Lieutenant unsealed the envelope all
sweaty and thankful. Under the full moon entering his room the
white pages had a silvery tint, like her body.

The pages erupted from the envelope - her long hair on his body.
Ellie was here and the Lieutenant was lost within such a vast presence, not knowing what he had truly read and what his imagination
had created. He laid the pages on the mattress, a brand new sheet
full of symbols. His perspiration caught the ink; his skin absorbed
her words – her touch on his shuddering body. He melted inside her,
muttering words he had never told her. His passion wrote letters
upon letters, letters which he never posted, letters which will never
be read.

*

For years, no matter how often he showers, every now and then a
symbol sprouts on his skin; random lone syllables which double his
conviction that Ellie will never go away.

Whenever some new girlfriend asks about these strange spots,
he murmurs: 'It is dermatitis, a stupid skin sickness, definitely not
contagious.'

*Belica Antonia Kubareli was born in Athens Greece, 1958. She has studied
literature and theater in Greece, sociology and creative writing in UK. She has
published six novels, several short stories, scripts and plays. Her works have got
national awards. She has translated approximately fifty books of Anglo speaking
authors, amongst which are: Jhumpa Lahiri, Salman Rushdie, Peter Carey,
Indra Sinha, Alan Spence, Zadie Smith, Helen Oyeyemi, Adichie Chimamanda
Ngozi, Joseph O' Connor, Joseph, Yann Martel, Nadine Gordimer, and others.*

Blue

By R.S. Varian

Most mornings she awoke before seven. Her alarm clock was set to go off at precisely seven in the morning. She liked being organised and being awake before her alarm went off gave her a sense of superiority. It maintained her order. She put on her dressing gown and made her bed. Folding the corners exactly and taking her time, she sharpened the folds to give a very precise, neat edge. Neatness was good. She strode to the bathroom and turned on the shower. She had read somewhere that hot water dulled the senses so, even though it was a freezing morning, she plunged into a cold shower without wasting the breath for a gasp.

She washed briskly; starting, as she did every morning, with her face and finishing with her feet. She did not enjoy touching her body, she thought it grotesque. Being naked was to be tolerated not enjoyed. Her eyes were shut as she organized the order of the day's tasks. She needed to be at work just before nine and had an after work appointment with her chiropractor at six. She needed to ring the vet about an appointment for her cat, she had to pop into the pharmacy to pick up mother's prescription and do the weekly shopping.

'Another day,' she mused as she bent down to scrub her feet. That is when she noticed that her feet had become brilliant blue. A deep clear blue, so blue and so pure was the colour it was almost indigo. It was as if someone had crept into her room during the night and painted them in her sleep. She had not had a person in her bedroom for over fifteen years so that was unlikely. Initially her heart started to hammer and her mind started to swing into panic, but she reigned in her reaction and reasoned her response. She uttered only the smallest of noise.

Slightly shaken, she dressed, ate her breakfast of wholemeal toast and black tea and left to catch the eight fifteen bus. On the bus her mind wandered back to her feet. She kept seeing the image over and over again in her mind. The whole episode had unnerved her. She got through the day but cancelled her chiropractor appointment on the off chance she may have needed to remove her socks.

The next morning she woke with the same routine of the day before. It was before seven and she rose swiftly turning off her alarm. It was a Tuesday, so like every other Tuesday she stripped the bed with seamless efficiency and remade it with fresh clean white sheets; its corners exact and the bedspread flat. She put the dirty sheets into the washing machine and went back to the shower. It was one of the virtues of living alone. She could have precise routines. She liked routine.

She had forgotten her feet until she plunged into the cold water and looked down. The blue had spread up her legs and it was almost to her hips. Her legs were blue. To say she was alarmed was an understatement, but, never one to waste undue emotion, she continued in the act of washing. She scrubbed her blue feet and legs furiously to see if they could be cleaned back to their original hue. They could not. Her legs felt fine – this was not a circulation issue. She did not feel unwell. She was slightly panicked. She methodically calmed her breathing down and went through her mental list of what was needed for the day. She needed to order photocopier toner from the stationary room; she had to meet with personnel over the new secretary she did not want; there was a meeting scheduled with her first line manger about the maternity leave for an office junior. After work she would visit her mother and have chicken soup and salad for supper - it was Tuesday after all. She did not once entertain the idea of going to see a doctor. She chose a brown trouser suit with brown boots to wear to the office.

After dinner that night with her mother, she drove home and folded the dry sheets from the morning's wash and went to undress for bed. She was relieved that the blue had stayed confined to the legs. Perhaps, she even countered, it was fading. On Tuesday evenings she made cocoa and read a novel in bed for twenty minutes precisely, and then turned out the lamp.

She woke later than normal on Wednesday morning. The alarm had just started to buzz. Startled by her laziness and ineptitude, she bounded out of bed in a hurry. She made her bed in her accustomed precise fashion and raced toward the shower a little on edge. It was when she reached into the cubicle to turn on the shower she noticed her arm. First she noticed her left arm and then with a squeal of comprehension her right. Her legs, including her feet and toenails, were completely blue and now her arms, from her shoulder blades to her finger tips, were also a deep shocking blue. She looked as if she had on long blue gloves and blue opaque stockings. She turned off the shower and quietly put on her dressing gown. She walked through to her kitchenette and sat. Without hesitation, she admitted to herself, she was concerned.

She rang the office and for the first time in twenty three years took a sick day. Not since her father died in 1991 had she taken a day off of work. Even when she had her annual holidays she went to work mentally and sometimes during her long weeks of vacation she dropped into work surreptitiously just to check on 'this' or 'that'. Her holidays were periods to endure. A time when she went to her mother's, took care of the maintenance jobs around the house, and a time when she took long walks to the local shops just to watch other people catch the bus to work. She did not like down-time, it was a waste. She hated waste.

Even though her body was almost entirely blue she still did not entertain the idea of visiting a doctor or health professional. She thought instead of going to the library and researching this herself, to see if turning blue had a name. She walked back to her bedroom and chose a shirt with large decorative cuffs and extra long sleeves; she buttoned the collar up at her neck and wore long trousers with ankle boots. She found a pair of gloves and scarf and was ready to go.

As she walked toward the front door and she looked in the mirror, and she habitually checked every morning before leaving. To the outside world her condition was not obvious. With a gloved hand she flicked away a strand of hair on her cheek and noticed, with a sickening heart, something odd under her left eye. It was a dot, a small perfectly formed dot. She had no time to lose. She headed straight for the library and hopefully towards an answer.

At twelve thirty she walked out from the quiet air of the library into the fresh winds of early winter. She had been in the library since it opened and had found nothing. There was Alaskan folklore about two twins that were born blue, and a Hindu god, Ganesh. But no reports of any skin colour changing disease. She caught the bus home.

On gently snibbing the lock of her front door, she walked over to the hall mirror and removed her gloves and scarf. She knew she was turning blue. What she did not know was why. She dreaded going to bed that night because all that was left was her face and torso. How could you cover your face? She had lived such a good life. Such an organised life. She had made her life exemplary. She did not lie, she gave to charity, attended church and she ate wholemeal and organic foods. She looked after her elderly mother and she cared for her cat. She worked hard and diligently all her life and there she was turning blue.

She rang her mother and gave a feeble excuse of not being able to come over. She promised she would make it up to her tomorrow. She explained that some time ago she had put frozen meals in her freezer for just such an occasion. She explained to her mother in a belittling voice that she should reheat one of these dinners but 'please be careful when pulling the plate out of the oven'.

Her mother was mildly surprised. It had been a long time since her daughter had not come over for her evening meal. She enquired gently if it was a man. Her mother enquired with laughter in her voice but hope in her heart. Her daughter did not dignify the question with a response. Her mother held secret fears that her daughter did not like men. Her daughter, as far as she knew, had never so much as had a date, let alone a boyfriend. When she was a teenager she did not put posters on the wall like other girls. To her mother's knowledge, she had never had a crush or a fantasy about anyone male or female. Her mother thought that she should broach the subject, letting her know that it would be alright if she liked women. In fact it would be good, great even. It would be so much better than being alone. But, how do you start that conversation?

After watching television, a past-time she did not fully enjoy or understand, she decided to have a shower before retiring to bed. Her bones were unusually cold and beginning to ache. She was heavy. This break from her routine was crippling. She ran the shower hot until she had fog and mist in the bathroom. She dropped her clothes messily in a heap on the bathroom floor; she entered into the hot steamy water of the shower and let out a low guttural sigh of relief. The pleasure was overwhelming. She let the water soak through her skin. She moved about the shower cubicle letting the water hit different parts of her body. She held her neck forward so the hot water ran down her back. Her toes started to tingle, her arms started to pulsate with feeling.

After the shower she dressed in fleecy long pyjamas and put socks on her feet and gloves back on her hands. She hopped into bed wanting to be warm. She could not bear the strange coldness of her body. After a few minutes she pushed her blankets back and walked over to the central heating. She turned it up. She padded into her kitchenette and flicked on the kettle, she decided a hot water bottle might help.

It was impossible to keep her bed covers in pristine order while wearing all of the clothes. With the hot water bottle close to her skin and her teeth chattering with cold she let it all go. She escaped the neatness, the order and the regime of perfection. Lying there quietly in her bed on Wednesday night she was aware for the first time ever that she was alone in a big bed.

R.S. Varian is originally from warmer sunnier climes and is currently freezing to death in Dundee. She has four terrific children and a patient, understanding husband, who have supported her short publishing career so far.

Medical Records

By Andrew Murray Scott

Robert glides past the open window hatch.
I creak back in my chair, sip coffee –
he intones the same bars of the same song,
and again blurs the light in my window.

His voice sounds hollow, almost eerie
in the green & beige tiled corridor,
head sideways, he grins secretly
like a crocodile on a riverbank.

Sunshine from the car park, muted
in the psychiatric unit, the gentle hum
of summer, a persistent bluebottle.
Somewhere the clash of a meals' trolley,
someone drops a steel dish.

And here I sit, enthroned –
lord of the files, master of the monthly stats,
shuffling paper: in-patient, out-patient,
sole keeper of the ECT log-book,
imagining all the places my thoughts can reach.

At least the residents have expectations
the next medication, mealtimes,
and some will be released
into the community, become well
resume exciting lives.

But not Robert perhaps, at least
not until he learns a new song -
and then learns to sing.

Andrew Murray Scott is the author of four novels: Tumulus, Estuary Blue, The Mushroom Club, and The Big J, as well as ten non-fiction books, including biographies of John Graham of Claverhouse, Alexander Trocchi, the 'enfant terrible' of modern Scottish writing, and various books about Dundee. His first novel, Tumulus, won the inaugural Dundee Book Prize in 1999 and was subsequently listed in 'The Other Hundred' of the 100 Best Scottish Books compiled by Professor Willy Maley in association with the Scottish Book Trust.

Jury and Duty
By Anna Day

She rolls over in bed, her side typically neat as she looks down at her body, flat and small under the duvet. Her husband Peter's side, is askew and messy, the result of his night spent turning and grunting in bed.

They decided to get separate duvets after six months of marriage. Their incompatible sleeping habits left her cold and him irritated, so they bought two duvets and the problem was solved. At first they were manoeuvred into matching covers, but now he has a masculine stripe in wine red and black. Hers is a duck egg blue. Because Peter had claimed that he never knew which was his.

She told her counsellor (provided and paid for by HM Government, according to the headed notepaper) that she hadn't slept since the trial, but she is almost sure this is a lie. The line between sleep and wake seems blurred almost all the time, even when she is doing things that require her, without a doubt, to be awake: such as driving or cooking or talking. She knows she must have been asleep in the night, simply because she doesn't feel as if she has been lying here

for hours and hours, but the memories and the dreams are too
similar to tell them apart.

The house sounds empty as soon as the door slams behind Peter,
despite the radio muttering early morning traffic advice. His daily
trail of debris sneaks around the house and, before she even empties
her bladder in the morning, she repairs the damage he has caused.
When she was working she did this in a hurry, but today and
every day for the foreseeable future, she takes her time over every
task just to fill the hours. Stopping herself from peeing is a vicious
delight too. She's never been in the house alone for more than a
day since they moved in together seven years ago. Peter's holidays
are prescribed by the company, which closes down for two weeks at
Christmas, a week at Easter and two weeks in the summer. Each
January, on the first day back from the Christmas holidays, she
would get in to the cold office early to be first to mark her days off
on the holiday rota to ensure their time off matches.

She's seeing the counsellor at two which means leaving the house
at 12:30. It's only a thirty minute journey, but she wants to ensure
that she can stop, if she needs to, and find a car parking space. It's
still early and she has four and a half hours to fill before she leaves
with nothing to do. Amanda wonders if it would be rude to knock
on the door of her neighbour's house and offer to weed their garden
while they're at work. They've got such a lovely space, with a much
bigger patio than hers and, she suspects, a hot tub, but all the gazing
from the upstairs bedroom window has failed to convince her. She
can only see a corner of what could be a hot tub or when she is
being less generous, a very well contained compost heap. She neither
wondered nor cared before, but staring through the overgrown tree
trying to gauge the likelihood of a hot tub in a suburban street has
taken up several hours of her time in recent weeks. But she may
never know as Jim and Carol haven't, beyond releasing their first
names, made overtures to becoming friends in all their years living
next door to each other. She supposes offering to do their garden,
simply because the bit she can see properly is a complete mess and
therefore getting on her tits, would be slightly odd.

Her own house is immaculate. It's always been neat but she's
always said – and Peter has agreed with his usual eloquence, a

nod or grunt – that old houses are never 'done'. There's always a job needing doing – painting that needs touched up, grouting, a bit of damp to see to. She supposes that it's the same in new houses, but really she hasn't a clue. She and Peter moved here after they got married, which was two years after they got engaged, which was two years after they met. They've lived here ever since, in the cottage bungalow. She thinks of it as sweet, cosy. Three bedrooms is more than enough when it's just the two of them, though Peter talks about turning one room into a gym. But when she was first home, before the exhaustion flowed in, she cleaned and mended and painted. Every drawer and cupboard was exhumed and cleared, before being placed back in its old place, smarter and tidier but just as ignored.

Walls were repainted, in the same magnolia the entire house was bathed in, neutral neutral neutral. The sofas were beige – which made Peter very jumpy on the odd occasion a friend came round to visit with a baby or toddler in tow – and the floors were pine laminate, sparkling, unmarked.

Now there was nothing left to do, beyond the everyday tasks, but that was okay as the tiredness was constant. She was in bed most evenings by nine, wakening gently when Peter went at seven the next morning. Then the day would pass in a semi comatose blur, staring at the garden or the walls or sometimes the TV. But she found the jolly daytime TV voices an irritant so usually the house was silent.

Leaving the house was almost impossibly tiring. The 'doing' was bearable, but the choices were terrifying. What to wear, whether to wash her hair or simply tie it up, whether to drive and risk falling asleep at the wheel or whether to take the bus and bump into somebody she knew, somebody Peter knew, or, worst of all, some friend of her parents. Possibly, if she was very unlucky, her mother or father themselves.

She was driving today. Then she could stop at Morrison's on the way home, if she had the energy, and 'do a shop'. Pick up all the necessary bags of frozen and ready meals she'd need to feed them for another week, cooking with the very least amount of effort, simply turning an oven on and placing the edibles on a throw away baking tray. Carefully timed so that the oven would ping in the final moments before Peter came home. Not so that she'd have food on the table to welcome him, as he thought, but in case she fell asleep, so the house wouldn't burn down, Peter would save her.

Therapy had been suggested two months after her trial had finished, when the antidepressants seemed to be having no effect and it was obvious that she wasn't the same measured, calm but friendly, out going part of the couple. Now Pete was left to make all the conversational running. So the doctor had called the police liaison officer and within the week she'd found herself in a room of strangers, each talking about their trial and their inability to continue normal life, long after they had declared guilty or not guilty. Not that the trials were theirs, as such. None of the people were criminals – or had ever been accused of a crime – but were members of the jury. Called upon at random to judge, without training, a person or persons who had been accused of a crime. They had each gone to court thinking about their civic duty, or time off work, or a vicarious thrill or just plain nosiness, but each had emerged from the claustrophobic, uncomfortable jury box as a changed person. Nobody had expected to see such horrors.

The phone rang once when she was in the bath, which was more effort to prepare than a shower that simply required a switching of a switch. All the testing and topping up with cold water, then a drop more hot and the different lotions and potions that could be added was an exhausting process of a bath, but ultimately more satisfying and it took longer, ate up more of her day.

It rang again while she was drying her hair, but she didn't hear it, then once more when she was sat back on the beige sofa, deciding whether to eat before she left or not. She thought about picking it up, but instead, listened to the tinny ring booming out of the silence, until it was too late and it had stopped.

Peter arrived home seven minutes before she was due to leave for town. 'Have you been made redundant?' she immediately asked. This was the first time he'd come home early since he'd had to take a half day for the funeral of a school friend, probably someone counted as a best friend in a bigger life.

'No, I thought I'd give you a lift to town. I did try to call. It will

save you parking. Then I'll go and get those new tyres fitted and
pick you up. It's an hour, the session, isn't it?'

She knew better than to show surprise. Doing so would indicate
that she thought him often thoughtless, crass. 'Thank you,' she
said, and went to sit in the car while he checked the back doors and
all the windows, making sure they were locked.

*

Amanda's trial had lasted for 127 days and was to determine
the guilt or innocence of Amal Al Sahid, Jamal Jannis and Emirt
Ali Alaumo. The three men and two of their friends, all in their
twenties had, allegedly, filled their jacket pockets with nails,
strapped themselves into rucksacks filled with explosives and
entered a pub near Leeds University early on the evening of Friday
12th March. Two of the boys exploded almost simultaneously, killing
themselves and fifteen drinkers. They injured a further fifty-six,
six of whom subsequently died of their injuries. Al Sahid suffered
severe burns and a broken leg, Jannis was left blind but Ali Alaumo
left the scene uninjured.

The jury heard the stories of each of the survivors – a quiet Friday
night drink with a new partner before moving to a local restaurant,
a post work pint, a catch up with schoolfriends, a barman about
to return to New Zealand to see his sister marry, working his last
shift. They heard, through many voices, the stories of the dead –
the relationship that could have gone somewhere, the widow, the
orphan, the parent who lost three daughters, meeting for a quick
stiffener before attending an appalling sounding family party.

The jury retraced the steps of the bombers, saw where the pub
had been, where now a small remembrance garden sat instead.
There was CCTV footage of people running from the pub, the blood,
the screams, the limbs and skin. Jury members saw more than
1,544 photos, from the scene, of the dead bodies and the injured,
still lying waiting for help. They saw the makeshift morgue and
the boards and everything the newspapers hadn't been allowed to
report, as it was just too upsetting to be showing people as they sat
at home or on the tube or eating their lunch. Day after day, image
after image, they sat and saw.

The testimonials from the defence were the most terrifying to

Amanda. Even if she wasn't allowed to admit it, she had already decided the men were guilty, which turned out to be a unanimous decision, and she failed to understand how the gentle mother who spoke so lovingly of her son, her baby, could produce a monster. The men themselves took the stand with a reluctant swagger. Two refused to look at the jury at all, but Al Sahid, with his distorted, wizened face, like he'd buffed his skin up to a sheen, caught the eye of each member of the jury one by one, daring them to blink first.

The men had all been found guilty and sentenced to life without parole.

*

Amanda arrived at therapy twenty-four minutes early.

Jury and Duty is an extract from Anna Day's first novel. Anna Day is Director of Literary Dundee, an organisation which includes the Dundee International Book Prize, The Dundee Literary Festival, Dundee Literary Salons and many other events. She also runs Dundee University Press. She lives with a husband, a daughter and a dog.

Ten O'Clock News

By Nicky Guthrie

The starving woman looks but is elsewhere,
Her quiet baby peaceful in her arms.
Serene. No pleading eyes, no upturned palms,
Her life beyond the pain that she can bear.
Her struggle's past, she does not look to find
Her errant husband, son; she saw them leave
Their torn and tattered bodies, does not grieve.
She's handsome and she does not seem to mind.
Turn down the sound and fetch a glass of red,
A comfort snack before you go to bed.
Get cosy on the sofa with your man,
Your bodies pressed together while you plan
To put the world to rights; complacent, wise,
While in another world, her baby dies.

Nicky Guthrie lives above the snow line in the Highlands with a variety of two and four legged companions and is trying to figure out how best to manage one's life given the unpredictable and unstable nature of time and space. She has two daughters whose knowledge has far outstripped her own. She feels infinitely blessed.

The Last Visit

By Brian Meechan

The rusty metal creaks, as the decaying swing gently rocks. A withered man sits on it, hunched over, slowly going back and forth. He pulls up the lapels of his thick brown winter coat as a protection against the wind- his only company in the barren swing park. He tips his brown flat cap further down. His eyes now the only part of his face exposed. They're too cold, too tired, to reflect much of anything.

He doesn't notice the creak of the swing. All he hears are the sounds that haunt him, whether awake or asleep.

Calm: peace, contentment. He clings to those fleeting seconds in his memory. Before they escaped him forever.

Then the sounds. The screech. The thud. The woman's scream.

Back and forth. Ice lies beneath his feet at the park. He scrapes his shoes along it, ignoring the hazard. He looks down at the picture he holds in his hands.

The screech. The thud. The woman's scream. His mind flashed a message as the world slowed around him: Nothing good comes after now. He remembers turning, looking back up the street where he'd left them. A scene was unfolding on the road; the parents who'd been playing in the swing park sheltered their children from the sight.

Back and forth. The man stares down at the picture in his hands. The face of a proud young father and his beaming toddler gives the tattered photograph an unusual glow.

He'd walked to where people had gathered. Not run, like they do in the movies, but walked. Each step weighed heavier as he looked around for an escape route from the thought that was forming in his mind. He hoped for a glimpse of Mark shielding Jake like the other parents were doing. Or, if he knew his son, more likely running to help.

He felt the bile rise from his stomach. The only thing that stopped him from throwing up was the invisible fist that clenched his throat.

He reached the devastation. An imposing grey car, its front caved in, its windscreen shattered. The door ajar. A woman stood: shaking, crying, mumbling.

The man looks down at the twisted torso of his son, not long a man himself. Next to him, the still body of his grandson. A trickle of blood flows through his blonde hair and forms a pool between the two of them.

The driver had been reaching for a ringing mobile. The child had heard the inviting chimes of an ice cream van and bolted. The father, engrossed in a conversation with an old friend, was slow to react.

There were lots of witnesses.

The child had frozen in the road, as the car hurtled towards him. The driver looked up and slammed on the brakes. The father dived for the boy, taking the full force of the blow from the car as he grabbed him. He couldn't hold on. His son flew out of his arms, onto the bonnet and into the windscreen that smashed into pieces. The woman screamed.

Flash of a second... tragic accident... nothing to be done. They said.

Time heals... it'll get easier. They said.

Case closed. Move on. They meant.

Back and forth. He stares at the photo of the two of them as he swings. He looks at it for hours every day hoping it will wipe, at least for a few seconds, his final image of them.

The swing beside him has a broken chain. It's thrown over the bar at the top. It leaves the seat dangling above him, like a hangman's noose.

Four years had come and gone. He avoided walking past the park, or even near it, whenever he could.

This was where he brought his son when he was a boy. The park he'd brought his grandson to. The one they'd been heading for when they left him on that August morning after their visit.

The gates of the park are closed now. A sign reads:
CONDEMNED FOR DEMOLITION.

Brian Meechan is a political journalist who works on TV, radio and online. Born and raised in Glasgow, he studied Sociology at Glasgow University. He's since worked for ITN and the BBC and studied at Cardiff University and Edinburgh Napier University. He now lives in Wales. When not immersed in the world of politics, he writes short stories and screenplays. He's currently working on getting one of his short film scripts produced.

The Drawn Blinds

By Eddie Small

Her house was known for the drawn blinds. Only the merest hint of sunlight, which poked and spiked itself through cracks and fissures, was allowed entry. She had as much desire not to see out as she had to prevent the outside world from looking in. The once-yellow blinds had remained closed for over fifteen years now, and thick dust clung in clumps, and, at certain times of day, when the sun was spearing in the right direction, the surface seemed like a grey snow-scene. The cobwebs at the top, on either side, were newer; she'd broken the shaft of her feather duster when she fell over her chair in the semi-darkness of the early afternoon. That was over seven years ago, and she'd bruised her hip and right shoulder heavily in the process. She enjoyed the painful bruising, covering her skin in a black-blue purple mosaic which hardly faded for a very long time. When she felt the bruising, she felt less of the constant ache from the crippling arthritis that smote her joints.

Only the chemist knew any of it; he knew the cream was for herself,

despite the fact that she always said she was collecting it for her
friend, Jessie. She called the chemist Andy from the very start,
even though his name was Alan, but he liked her far too much to
embarrass her by changing things. Alan's own mother had been
from the same era; she'd shared the same sensibilities, the same
selflessness, the same shame and dread of bothering a doctor. He
gave her the cream for free; told her it was old stock he'd wanted rid
of, and he watched with a bittersweet sense of sadness and pride
as this old lady made her way to the Post Office to collect the pension. She always seemed agitated when she went to collect her
pension money. Alan studied her, and could never stop seeing his
own mother. He'd watch her from behind, her narrow shoulders
turning in towards her chest, her back arching, and her aged large-
checked coat hanging in straight lines with considerable weight. Her
ancient hat was almost the same colour as the black, front-zipping,
once-fur-lined ankle boots which were older than himself. From the
back, Aggie Morris was desperately like his mother.

*

   Brian knew she was dead. Long before he had his wife call the
police to come and break the door down; he knew Aggie was dead
for he'd seen her earlier that morning. Aggie was his grandmother's
sister and she was also his next door neighbour. He guiltily
watched as an overweight police constable took three attempts to
break the flimsy lock on the apartment door; that flimsy yale lock
that had given an old woman her only semblance of security from
the world she so dreaded. She'd been going to bed before six in the
evening for many years now, and rising long before the alarm clock
flashed its silent five o'clock wakening call. She liked the quiet of
the mornings, and she felt little fear setting off to collect her single
bread roll from the all-night bakery. The half-mile walk took her
through some of Dundee's most dilapidated tenement buildings, and
they reminded her of the old days when the streets seemed always
to be populated with the comings and goings of these laconic, stour-
smelling shift-workers. Apart from these early mornings, the only
other time she'd venture out was her monthly visit to the Chemist's

shop, and on to the Post Office to collect her money, but that was always in the morning before ten. It was the night she'd hated. Now she wouldn't have to hate it ever again.

Her money felt damp, and smelled strongly of embrocation from the many opened tubes of the stuff strewn in the dresser drawers. It was a smell of mustiness and chloroform, of decay and stale urine; that was the smell from the old real-wooden drawers which she had filled with uncounted five and ten pound notes, thrown in as if she almost despised them. He remembered her telling him that money always reminded her of Archie. Without the notes there was no drinking, and without the drinking the thumpings would stop. Without the notes the beatings would stop. Brian found it difficult to believe her, but she was adamant and animated in a way that convinced him that his great-uncle Archie was maybe not the sainted man he'd always taken him for; at least, not when he'd had a drink. Sometimes it was hard to believe she was ever married. She'd looked every inch the ageing spinster, soured of the world and secretly yearning for the love which never came her way, and that's how he would remember her. He would now never know the she never was married. Her dark secret was safe now.

*

And now, twenty-seven years after Archie had been killed in a dockyard accident, his woman, Aggie, was being found by this overweight policeman; she was lying in her chair, her old holed hand-knitted cardigan stretched around her emaciated torso like a faded woolen shroud, and her tartan-tweed skirt draped very loosely over protruding hips. Her hat was still clinging to the lolling head like a feathered limpet. Her wrinkled mouth was parted at the pursed lips and her lifeless eyes were half-closed but seemed to have a fixed gaze on the old dresser.

The younger policeman came out of her house and told Brian she was dead. He feigned surprise. He wondered how he should react. The policeman asked him if he wanted to go in and see his great-aunt, and he made to enter her door, then he stopped. There was something so wrong with taking the money in his pockets back into the room from where it came. He turned and shook his head to the constable, and walked out. His own door was barely five steps away along the 'plettie'. He'd lived there for eighteen months now, something for which his grandmother had been very glad, for he could now keep an eye on her sister; her oldest sister who had been a worry ever since they'd called in one day and found her unconscious with a dried out pan glowing deep red on the gas stove. At first he'd called in every second tea-time. He'd call out first before he opened the door with the key that she had been so reluctant for him to have. Then it became once a week; on the days he was going to the super-market. And he would collect her pitifully few groceries and take them to her. She would tell him where he'd find money. And he did.

His wife, Lisa, accompanied the officers back into Aggie's house, but they were all shuffled back out when the female doctor arrived to examine the old soul's body. The fat policeman re-entered Brian's house and asked a few routine questions in a singularly uninterested fashion; it was already twenty minutes after his normal breakfast time and his big belly was craving fried bread with baked beans. Brian felt clammy and troubled.

No, he hadn't seen her since last week. Yes, he did have a key, but it had completely slipped their mind in the panic.

The policeman looked at him scathingly, and rubbed a smarting shoulder at the thought of this forgotten key. The questions stopped and he was glad. A cough entered the door, followed closely by the doctor who announced she was finished. Brian was given a note and Lisa rang the undertaker whose premises were in the next street but one.

She was gone within the hour; well, her body was. A matter of two minutes after the undertaker had taken Aggie's remains, a couple of her nieces had arrived alerted by Lisa's telephone call. It was Saturday, and their husbands hadn't bothered to come with them. They were too busy drinking in The Mariner's Bar, not much more than a mile away. The two nieces had been too late to see Aggie in the flesh, but then they hadn't done for many years. After a couple of minutes of small-talk, they all trooped in to the house of the eternal twilight. The chair she had been sitting in looked strangely aggressive; its stains on the tight-tufted worn fabric looking like a face twisted into a demonic leer. He shuddered, and turned, and the four-drawered dresser made him shudder again. One of his aunts forced open the drawn blinds cascading a mulch of death-grey flotsam into the already choking, airless, nauseous atmosphere. The women went over the place, tutting and holding their noses whilst rummaging like two practised burglars. They found nothing that interested them; they couldn't have, for he had it in his pockets and he could feel the distinct heat on each of his thighs but the redness was in his cheeks.

He got away with the redness, for he was always the soft lump who cried first at funerals. They suspected nothing, for they had no reason to expect anything other than the old chipped ornaments and tattered photo albums which they didn't even bother to open. Time enough for that later, they lied. They left after an hour and he left with them, closing the door without looking back.

Brian went back that afternoon, and drew her blinds.

Eddie Small lives in Perth, but hails from Dundee, where, for the past several years he has studied at the University. He recently started his PhD research on Religion and the Scottish Funeral, but he is also a committed writer who loves to dabble in various writing genres. An appearance at the Edinburgh Book Festival last year, where he read some of his work alongside others from the University, whetted an already keen appetite for writing and for life. He is currently involved in writing a 'what's happened so far' article for the Literary Dundee website.

Oxfam Footwear

By Helen Howe

On a low shelf, away
from the window display -
brown leather shoes:
pitted, ash-bark gnarled
and lustreless, curled
almost, witchy-pointed toes.

Whose were they to amble
in? Which paths were trampled?
What time-span measured?
Uncomfortable on me:
feet mould differently,
too much give - no pressure.

Slack straps hug the buckles,
the thick ankles
now forgotten.
Heels down on the instep
(baby on the right hip
grown up and gone).

I picture her: a wife,
tumid, languid with life;
shabby reflection shows
in Clarks' sparkling window -
slips in on a whim, now,
to buy new shoes.

Helen Howe was born in 1965 and grew up in a north Derbyshire mining community. She graduated last year from the Open University after studying English Language and Creative Writing. Now living near Sheffield, she works as a musician and youth worker. She has recently had short stories published in Flash and First Edition magazines, and is currently writing her first novel.

Wonderberries
By Lorraine McCann

H e took more painkillers and lay down on the sofa for a nap. He knew it was a kind of luxury, a late-morning suspension in warm opiate. But even now, already, after just two days at home, he'd come to depend on checking out like this for an hour or so.

When he woke up, his mouth was dry and tacky and the weather had turned a promising sky into a blank grey wash. He sat up and supposed he should eat something. Gathering his crutches into place, he hauled himself up and lurched through to the kitchen. There he found mushroom cup-a-soups, some blocky orange cheese and some bread. Got the kettle, took the lid off and held it underneath the tap.

As he listened to the pouring water, he looked out at the garden and saw the greenhouse. Heather's greenhouse. A place he'd not been in almost since he assembled it for her all those years ago. Something he didn't understand had made him not like that gardening thing even as a kid, when his granddad tried to get him

to grow tomatoes in a sack. Was it the thick, earthy air? The dusty
residue? Maybe the smell of overheated plastic releasing vague
toxins into the air. Or the spindly little green things that all looked
annoyingly the same, but weren't.

He drank the soup, which refused to thicken, then made some
tea and a cheese sandwich. He took these, with difficulty, out to the
patio and sat on a low brick wall; cuddling his mug as he rested his
bad leg straight out in front of him.

The pain was presently far away like a distant siren, but it would
be on its way back soon, and the thought made him nauseous. Or it
could have been the pills. He shook his head slightly, and pressed
his thumb and forefinger into his eye-sockets. The greenhouse
spangled for a few moments and then drew back into focus. It was
maybe twenty feet away, but these distances were meaningful now.

He put his mug down and decided to make the trek. Three steps
up to the lawn. Five stepping stones in the grass. A near-impossible
side-step along past the mini-goal he and Jack had set up last
summer. By the time he got to the greenhouse door, his armpits
were drenched. But he made it. He wiped his mouth with the sleeve
of his fleece and reached for the little silver door handle. And that
was when he saw the lock.

Heather's greenhouse – a place he never went – a place she knew
he never went – with a small brass padlock on the door.

He stared at it, his breathing still uneven. The neighbours' windows
suddenly seemed to be everywhere, as if his right of access to his
own home was in doubt. The dull fiery beat in his heel pulsed and
nagged and leeched him of the patience to wait and ask why, after
years of no barriers between them, there was now a barrier between
them.

Back in the house, he collected a big screwdriver, an adjustable
wrench and a pair of pliers, slid these into his cargo pockets and
headed back out to the garden.

The padlock was a bit fiddly but it wasn't strong; within a minute
or two it was bust.

The air smelled exactly as he remembered, but with a sweetness
that came from Heather's perfume. He cast an eye over neat rows
of seedlings, some under plastic covers, all with little white or grey

labels at the back. A small pink-seated stool stood in the middle of the space, in front of an empty square foot of aluminium bench. It had a light covering of dry compost in which he could still see the marks from his wife's hand as she'd swept it clear.

He looked up through the glass and back towards the house, which seemed to have receded even further; like he was drifting and it was dry land. Then he turned back towards the stool, drew it aside to sit on it, and found himself looking at a little red bucket and spade.

His breath left his body in an instant and he let himself flop down hard onto the stool. It shook and skittered a bit along the flagstone, but his eyes stayed on the bucket and spade. The same ones. They had to be the same ones.

He bent down and picked them up. The spade inside the bucket. Light and solid and red. The bucket had sand in the corners of the turrets at the bottom. He pressed his index finger into it, then brought it out and looked. Fine and white. Play sand. He rubbed his finger and thumb together and the grains fell onto the bench. The spade, with its triangular handle. All he could see was Tom's square, dimpled little hand. No memory of Jack ever playing with this. No memory at all.

He put the spade gently back inside the bucket and then rested them both back under the bench, next to a slim metal plan cabinet. It had been a good few years since he'd seen that too, he thought, as he ran his finger along its neatly folded edge. He slid open the top drawer. In there were some rubber bands and a packet of lettuce seeds. He shut the drawer again and pulled open the next one down. That was empty. Knowing there were eighteen drawers in this thing, he bent over to see if any of them were labelled in Heather's innocent, schoolteacher hand:

'Lady's Fingers.' 'Love in a Mist.' 'Cotoneaster.' 'Wonderberries.'

His head filled with a vision of gigantic superhero raspberries.

He pulled open the drawer. It contained a green exercise book with 'Wonderberries' written on the cover. He took this out and opened it up, causing a newspaper clipping to fall into his lap. A dry and discoloured 'Plant of the Week' column about wonderberries.

He turned it over in his hands and then went back to the book.

On the first page, Heather had drawn a sketch. It was good. A cluster of plump, round berries bunched together like cherry tomatoes. On the line underneath she'd written: 'Solanum burbankii'. And then, further down: 'Mr Palosi grows these next to tomatoes. Very thin skin, like a concord grape. Easily bruised. Poisonous if harvested too soon.'

This took up half a page. He turned over. The next page was blank, as was the one after that. But the book had the uneven bulk of cheap paper heavily written on with Biro, so he riffled through it, and quickly found the writing that began halfway through. His wife's hand, but altered. Ragged. Serrated.

'I can't keep this inside. I can't keep it inside but I can't let it out either. It's not fair to let it out but it's all the things I want to say that aren't fair but I want to say them anyway because this isn't fair. I can't even whisper the thing that I can't say. That I blame him. Because I do. And I'm sorry because I know no one could ever be more sorry than he is but I do blame him. I just just do.'

As he read, he heard in his mind for the millionth time, that knock at the door.

*

He is sitting by the side of the bath in which his son Tom is playing. He knows the person at the door has something Heather needs, and that it will not take him long to get it. 'How long could it take?' he thinks, as he looks at his son. He thinks, 'He's not a baby anymore. He can walk and stand. He'll be fine.'

He will explain to the person at the door that Tom is in the bath. A second knock at the door. He stands up. He considers telling Tom not to move, but decides against it as children usually do the opposite of what they are told. So he just casually says, 'Daddy will be back in a second.' He takes the stairs three at a time and yanks open the door.

He is not gone long.

He hurries at all times.

He comes back into the bathroom and time has vanished. Everything has to happen at once. But even when it does, it's too late.

*

He lowered the book back onto the bench and pressed it shut, to suffocate its whisperings. The skin on his shoulders crawled with realisation. All the times she'd come out here by herself, only God knows how many nights or mornings or afternoons when he was doing God knows what, and she'd sat here and written this. The state of her. Her hands shaking so much the pen wouldn't stay on the paper. His girl, alone with this. His poor girl.

He went back into the house and waited for his family to come home. When they did, they had tea together and talked about their day. He said he'd mostly slept.

When Heather came downstairs later after putting Jack to bed, he was at the kitchen table reading the evening paper. Heather poured herself a glass of red wine.

'Anything?' she asked, looking over his shoulder.

Alan murmured something about the bridge being closed at the weekend.

'Does that mean we don't have to take Jack karting?' she said.

He didn't reply. She put her glass down on the table and stood with her hands on the back of a chair.

'Look', she said, 'I was serious when I said I don't think you should be playing football at your age.'

He nodded, and leaned his elbows on the paper, his fingertips against his temples, like a shield. He didn't have to look at her to know her green eyes would be sparkling in the way they did when she really wanted her way. When she was usually right. When she was entitled to be.

'Oh, by the way', he said from under his hands. 'That cat from next door managed to dig its way into the greenhouse. I had to break the lock to get it out.'

Heather didn't say anything.

'I'll get you another one, okay?' he said.

He could hear her swallow.

'I only put it on because there's weed killer in there', she said.

Then she put her hand out and stroked his hair.

'That's what I thought', he said. 'I thought it would be something like that.'

Lorraine McCann was born in Dundee in 1964. After studying English at Dundee University, she worked in publishing in Edinburgh, where she is now a freelance writer and actor. She wrote the dramas 'A Rose for Chopin' (2002) and 'The Trading Game' (2004) for BBC Radio 4, and several successful one-act comedies for fringe theatre. Her debut novel, Centrepiece, was shortlisted for the inaugural Dundee Book Prize (1999) and subsequently published. In 2008, she won first prize in the prestigious Brian Moore Short Story Competition. She is currently working on a new novel and a full-length play.

The Cat
By Christopher Reid

There was no letting about it: no cautious
loosening of drawstrings, no tipping up
and shaking out. The cat stepped forth
of its own accord. With a yawn
that had a snarl in it, and an absent-minded
hoisting of its tail, already it looked bored
with the fact of its own existence.
So? What else was new?
The disdain, the brusqueness, the lack of tact
of your typical, blunt-headed tom:
all present and correct!
Just time to allow its arched and writhing
back to be stroked, an attempt at tenderness
acknowledged with a petulant squawk,
and the next minute it had left by the window –
away, I dare say, to some other
pressing errand of unsubtle innuendo.

Christopher Reid teaches at the University of Hull. He has won several awards including the Eric Gregory Award, the Somerset Maugham Award, the Hawthornden Prize and a Cholmondeley Award. His latest collection, A Scattering (2009), was shortlisted for the 2009 Forward Poetry Prize (Best Poetry Collection of the Year), the 2009 T. S. Eliot Prize, and won the 2009 Costa Book of the Year. He has a number of poetry collections and two books of poetry for children. Reid is often sighted as a co-founder of the 'Martian School' of poetry and has also published illustrations in Punch and London Magazine.

Earwigs
by Jim Stewart

The gathering of dark T-shirts from the line
on a day turned cold
is followed by a shaking out of earwigs
onto the pale floor,
the loss of anywhere to hide
hard on crevice dwellers
which winter at times in cracks,
bodies flat and wedged
lengthwise into splits,
or see out the short days
and the frozen nights
huddled in dead heads.
But scattered from the wrong folds
under strange light,
and radiating from where they dropped
lost and single on the lino,
they stop bewildered
on this great space,
useless forks
raised against the shake-out of the days.

Jim Stewart was born in Dundee in 1952, and co-teaches Creative Writing at Dundee University, where he has given teaching assistance since the late 1980s. He publishes poems from time to time in various outlets.

Swallows
By Andrew Rubens

The swallows flitted in and out of the bleached whale-skeleton timber of the unfinished attic all month. Unfettered by gravity, their weaving entrances and exits between the ribs of the roofs underlined the clumsy weight of our ladders and footboards. Seeming unperturbed by the tattoos of hammer drumming and machine noise, they rested on the rafters in between foraging expeditions, oblivious or uncaring of their occasional audience. They exhilarated in the air's freedom, pirhouetting and somersaulting over the site like spiralling fireworks about to burst.

The rain did not daunt them. While we huddled beneath the beams, earthbound, in frustrated resignation, they flickered over our heads, returning from wet sorties with stuffed beaks: flies, aphids, prize hymenoptera. And, as we were to realise, grass, moss, mud and feathers. While our work progressed upwards, the swallows conducted their own architecture.

We reached the attic, bending ourselves over the horizontal timbers, pouring awkwardly through bolted frames and balancing on the bare rafters. In the far corner, the eaves protected their organic ornament, a soup-bowl the colour of peat. The nest's completeness cast our grand designs into absurdity. It was as if we were building a giant ark simply to protect its perfection.

'Building regulations. If they knew the birds had nested, we'd have to wait for the fledglings to leave. The job would have to stop for months.'

I was chosen. My dirty anorak, the colour of mustard, hid me from the steel sky and the drizzle as I clambered among the struts. Through the gaps between my legs I could see down to the concrete floor three stories below. The swallows were not home. They were swooping in the dreich, performing dizzying dogfights with gnats and midges. I had often sneaked up here to watch them, fixated by their delicacy – they looked like jaded toys; forlorn, dustied Christmas tree decorations. But the metal blue and burnt red-orange of their plumage shivered with life, and the black caviar-dots of their eyes shone with avian interest at their surroundings. They permitted a quiet human to approach within feet of them; I had captured their domesticity in grainy phone images. Now I approached their empty abode like a burglar finding an empty house unlocked.

The air was thick and strange all around me. I came close to the nest, round, brown and exact, mud, feathers, moss. Capable of meeting all their needs, separated from the praxis of our imaginations only by evolution. It was not too late to call the RSPB, or at least claim the fake conscience of hands washed.

I do not remember, now, how it finished. Whether I cupped my work-grimed hands around the tiny construction, solid yet fragile, carefully carrying it over the attic's bones before descending the ladder with excessive slowness, suffering the aggrieved looks of my harassed workmates as I lowered it with ritualistic attention onto the earth, source of its materials. Or whether I struck it in a swiping curvature with the claw end of my hammer, sending it cascading in crumpled, disintegrating pieces down to the floor below, and dust. Whichever course I took, it was a violent act, perhaps the most direct harm I have consciously caused to another being before or since (excepting insects). There was no living thing present to me, it was quiet, considered and condoned by those who were aware of it. The roof would be sealed, the eaves sheltered from the elements, the attic left to the dark and the spiders. Perhaps the swallows would find a new haven for their eggs, perhaps they would still have the time and the energy to build again. Perhaps not. In any case, the violence done was inerasable, indelibly committed to reality.

In the field of the stud farm next to the property, the horse screamed through its lungs, standing up against the fencing separating it from its companions a hundred metres off. Tossing its head anxiously, it followed their movements, pacing along the enclosure, back and forth.

Andrew Rubens studies English Literature and French at the University of Glasgow. He has worked as a labourer, a shelf stacker and a bicycle rickshaw driver. His interests include theatre, mountains, comics and the stories of refugees and the displaced. He would like to work as a writer. Next year he will be doing a research master's on the French-Romanian poet, essayist and visual artist Benjamin Fondane. He grew up on the Beano and his father is from Carnoustie.

The Quinces
By Kenneth Steven

That autumn we stayed in an old manse;
A place full of ticking clocks that sounded
Like disapproving Victorian gentlemen.

At breakfast between a hurry of bowls and courses
She told us of the laden trees in the garden,
All these quinces she hadn't time to pick.

Late that afternoon I went out
Under the blue-cold skies of October
A world closed in by trees and crows.

A low sun pierced the woods in a bonfire of light;
All round the house the lanes
Were gullies of red and gold leaves.

But that garden was yellow-white globes on branches
The colour of mistletoe berries, lamps of things
Shaped like pears.

Their stalks broke like ice,
Cracked in the frozen stillness-
I put them, piece by piece, in a basket.

I went back, wondering what her kitchen would smell like—
What things it would make for the winter—
The quince frothing in pans like lava.

Kenneth Steven is a full-time writer based in Dunkeld in Highland Perthshire. Some twenty of his books have appeared to date: poetry collections, novels and works in translation. In 2010 his volume of short fiction The Ice and Other Stories will be published by Argyll. Kenneth was awarded a second Hawthornden Fellowship in 2009. He travels all over the country undertaking readings and workshops for adults and youngsters alike.

Westerly
By Richard Lakin

The house stood on a jagged outcrop of rock, spotted with mustard lichen. It was built from huge blocks of granite. On the headland a black flag ran taut in the westerlies. Sea spray dashed against the rocks. Breakers retreated, spent, sucking running pebbles into the surf. Far out in the bay, white horses rode like flecks of titanium dabbed on canvas.

'You wouldn't want to be out there today', Dad said.

Dad unscrewed our flask. Steam rose from the hot coffee as it swirled into the plastic square-shaped cup. Dad had used this flask for years, so the white plastic had aged like bone. I shook my head. I hated the metallic taste flasks gave to hot drinks. Heaps of brown sugar couldn't shift it. On the horizon a yacht's sale dipped and rose. When I was six, Grandad had tacked a Jolly Roger to my bedroom wall. I'd dreamt of sunken Spanish galleons spilling pieces of eight onto the seabed. I'd read about giant squid drawing ships and their screaming crews into the ocean depths. I'd seen old maps, brittle and yellowed like paperbacks left in sunlight, showing unexplored lands and volcanoes and twisting serpents. And, always to the West, the words: 'Here Be Dragons.'

'Let's chuck some skimmers. Let's see what you're made of', Dad said.

He chose a smooth purplish stone that was flat as a roof tile. He threw it from palm to palm, gauging its weight. I picked up a pebble, tossed it in the air and caught it with a slap in my palm.

'Cheat. You can't use that', Dad said.

He pointed to an orange seam, striping the middle of the pebble.

'That's brick and the rest is cement. It's part of a wall, not a stone.'

I ran my fingertips over it.

'The sea has took off all the rough edges', Dad said.

He was wearing a tweed cap he'd bought from a farmer at the street market. The farmer had black teeth and a felt waistcoat with fishing flies in place of buttons.

'He saw you coming. Still, at least he can get his pegs sorted', Mum said.

Mum still called teeth 'pegs' like she did when I was a toddler. I still called most of her friends 'Auntie'. It just didn't feel right to change some things. Dad raised the peak of the cap. There was a line of grit; shining specks of sand plastered to his forehead with sticky sea salt. It reminded me of primary school when you glued outlines on sugar paper and let the sand fall across them, sticking, and creating a picture. Dad crouched low, braced his knees, and whipped his arm across his thigh, sending the pebble arcing into the waves. It missed the first breaker, flipped, and skimmed across the surface three times before plopping into the water.

'Fiver', Dad said.

I held up four fingers. We'd driven through the Bay to get here, but the Bay wasn't our thing. The beach was staked out with py-jama-striped windbreaks, beach towels and chubby, day-tripping families pouring orange squash from children's plastic teapots. An ice-cream van belched out diesel as its freezer unit chugged along in the heat. Its chimes stuck on: 'Jack and Jill went up the hill...' Divers and skippers of boats called 'Wet Dream' and 'Spent Pension' were shuffling for position on the jetty.

'They've got a few quid so they think they own the place', Dad said.

'I'm happy here', I said.

This rocky little cove was perfect. The rocks were amber and caramel and jagged and slick and smooth and lined like an ancient map. The constant scoring and scorching of the waves could barely change them. Smugglers and princes, perhaps even Vikings, had sat on these rocks. They were pitted and decked and pocked and spiked. They brought to mind the soft, wet mud of a farmer's field trampled by cattle and frosted by winter. I tapped my jeans pocket feeling the contours of my Moleskine notebook. Frosted by winter, I liked that.

Three boys were fishing on the point. Dad said we'd go and see what they'd caught. We hopped and slid and skated across rocks clumped with rich, brown seaweed.

'Any luck?' Dad said.

The eldest shook his head. He had a thatch of hair that looked as if no amount of gel or wax would ever tame it.

'What are you using as bait?'

The boy pointed to a handful of limpet shells at his feet. Dad pulled a face.

'You want rag or lug', he said.

The boy was using the drawstring from a raincoat as his line. Where it had frayed he'd singed it with a match or lighter and attached a large brass hook with flaking black paint.

He hooked a limpet and angled it downwards between a shelf of rock and a fringe of russet seaweed. The line hung loose. Fine grains of sand had washed into this pool as if the tide had been panning for gold. The line went taut. The boy allowed it to run a little. Then he pulled it and raised it by degrees hand over hand. A crab had the limpet between its pincers. Dad hopped from foot to foot.

'Let's see it', he said, crouching with a crack of the knees as the crab was set down on the rocks. Dad tousled the boy's hair. I doubted I'd ever make him that proud because I didn't fish or fight or run or jump. We left the boys to examine their prize. As we walked back across the headland Dad said: 'One day you'll have to show me what you write in those notebooks of yours.'

He smiled. I watched the black flag flutter, then drop. I didn't answer. People often smile when they're trying to make a serious point.

Richard Lakin trained as a chemist at Liverpool University before working as a policeman, a salesman and a journalist. He started writing to escape some of the routine horrors witnessed on night shifts in Birmingham and London. He is 34, married, and loves exploring the East Neuk of Fife and the beaches of Anglesey for buried treasure with his two boys. He also likes to stare out of train windows and catch fragments of conversation that might make stories.

Island Mink

By Jane Christie

Gradually, from the window,
the Minch waves at me – constant and grey.
It is no great occasion to spot you;
a flat liquid body as you swim landward.
Most likely (it is said) to rob eggs;
solitary and confident beside the sharp gull's nest.
We cannot imagine you sleeping,
or vulnerable amongst the twisting gorse –
You have no predators, no fatal flaw.
We will not witness your downfall.

Your reputation brings home stories of murderous
byres with ten, maybe twenty victims.
Mustel Vison – marauder, mutilator.
The gesticulated warnings fascinate me:
"shield the neck and do not corner".

One day, I see you on the hill
a snippet of immaculate black;
a brazen enemy on the rough
lichen. It is not enough.
This will bring no sharp intake of breath.
So I embroider you, in an heroic tapestry of sound:
On to eager ears at home and in icy playground chats
– your closeness is a white lie.
The pale hope of it all.

I expect to lose sight of you soon enough
but with the Minch, you grow
and diminish. Fleetingly pointing,
each time truth sticks in my throat.

The dark lies – vivid as your
imagined glare – all those years ago.

Jane Christie, a Dundee University graduate, has been an English teacher for twelve years and currently works at Craigie High School in the city. She lives with her husband and two young daughters in Carnoustie but was brought up in quite a different setting, on the Isle-of-Harris. The experience of growing up on the island, the powerful influence of the land and the fascinating stories she has heard from the locals -- often direct translations from gaelic -- provide much of her inspiration for writing.

Up Mendick Hill Again

By Douglas Bruton

Collum remembers a time before. He was just a boy and his Da woke him early one grey light morning. Pulled his brother out of sleep, too. Sandwiches were packed into a miner's canvas haversack and bottles of orange juice that the milkman had delivered to order whilst they'd slept, glass bottles with green foil tops.

'C'mon boys.' Collum's Da spoke in a hissed whisper, as though he did not want anyone else to hear. 'Quick as custard', he said. He was in a hurry to be off before the rest of the village went about its business.

The boys rose from their beds easier than usual and not just because it was the weekend. They dressed in silence, Collum and his older brother Andrew. Sleep, or more likely the occasion, stole their few words away. They did not look at each other across the bedroom, did not dare. They faced the yellow lamp-lit wall instead, watching their own thrown shadows there, and they dressed back to back.

They pulled the door to the cottage closed behind them when
they left and crept like thieves through the village. On tip toes, it
seemed like. Not a word spoken until they had left the houses behind
and had ventured out along rutted and grassy cart tracks that ran
down the side of enclosed fields.

'Pace yourselves', he said then. 'There's no hurry now.'

A whole day it took them, that's what Collum remembers. That's
what it felt like. Da led the way with Andrew careful in his footsteps
and Collum a little way back. But not so far that he could not hear
the stories his Da trailed behind him threaded on the air. Like
singing is how Collum remembers it now. Stories of his Da's own
boyhood, and that boy bringing sheep down off the hill for the
shepherd, and those sheep whistle-dog nipped and tucked into stone
pens at the edge of fields.

Collum's Da pointed to broken stones in the long grass and built
pens for the boys to see in the words that he spoke.

'The whole flock made ready for the coming of old Tam', he said.
'Old as stone and grey and small he was. Hair like silver spiders
in his ears and his face a map of all roads. And, wrapped in an
oiled cloth and tucked in his belt, old Tam had sprung shears, all to
make the big sheep small again.'

There were sheep in the fields as they walked. Collum could see
the sudden fright in their yellow eyes when they raised their heads
up from the grass. Heard it in their bleating, a sound like a baby
crying, a hundred babies, till the mist smothered them again.

There were cows in his Da's stories too. Slipperfield cows
steam-warm in early morning barns, and milk-teats pink and
pulled, and squeezing. The milk made music against the metal of
the buckets, that's the way he told it, and the froth on the fresh
milk was like old lace. And suddenly a girl called Mary was there.

They were not yet at the base of the hill when his Da started in
with his stories of a girl called Mary. Hair shiny and dark as coal
when it is new cut from the seam. That's how he described her.
White clean skin and her hand so small in his he was worried he
might crush it. Collum's Da had told him once about an injured
bird he had held in his closed palm. Its wing was broken and he
described holding it as though it was made of finest glass and he

could drop it if he did not take the care. When Collum closed his eyes he could see that cupped bird in his Da's hands, but he could not picture his Da with a girl out walking.

'Same as we are today. Same path, same hill. Chased her all my days it seemed. Always chasing her till she agreed to walk out with me to Mendick hill.'

And the girl called Mary and his Da climbed all the way to the top where they kissed, there for all the world to see, if the world was looking. Collum squinted to see the top of the hill. As if she might still be there, hidden in the low clouds, this Mary. As if this was why they were heading up Mendick hill with orange juice and sandwiches.

'That girl's your Mam', Collum's Da said to the boys, his voice dropped to a whisper again as though he was sharing a secret with them. Maybe there was a catch in his voice when he said it. There is in Collum's memory at least. And Andrew looked over his shoulder, quick as quick in case he was seen, and Collum following behind shrugged, not believing the girl could be his Mam or the boy his Da, and they kept on walking.

Collum recalls the climb only as a heaviness in his legs, and his breath coming short and snatched, and a pain in his side that he could not easily rub away. Slow was their progress and his Da was brought to a husky silence by his own exertions. Sometimes it was so steep they seemed to be crawling up the slope, on hands and knees but moving upwards. At their backs the morning opened up for them to see, except that they were focused on the way ahead and saw only grass and ferns and, higher on the hill, pink and white clover.

They stopped to eat their sandwiches when they were a little over half way up. The grass was still wet and the orange juice was warm. Collum remembers that, and how they sat in silence, the two boys watching their Da smoke a rolled cigarette he had lit with a Swan Vestas match nursed in the closed bowl of two hands.

When at last they had made it to the brow of the hill, they stopped to catch their breath and to wonder at what was all around them. The clouds had lifted. On the top of everything is what it felt like to Collum, and looking down on the whole of the world wherever

they turned. He could see the village, small and some distance
from where they were. Collum guessed which house was theirs,
though he couldn't be sure. Above, a blue sky stretched over everything,
burning and burnishing the far away hills to a blue-mist silver. He
looked to his Da standing tall and straight. Taller than he had ever
been, Collum thought. He was testing the wind with a raised wet
finger, turning it this way and that so it was like he was dancing,
a little like flat-foot pirouetting in the grass. And though Collum
stood too, tall as a boy can stand, and though he copied what his
Da did, copied it exactly, and Andrew did too, neither boy really
knew what he was testing for.

Then the ashes, his Mam's, a girl once called Mary, tipped out
on the wind so that they drifted like a grey ghost away from them.
That was it, the whole point of the climb. Afterwards, the boys and
their Da stood without saying a word, arms folded across one another,
and the world dissolved before them.

*

Now, years have been added to years, so many that Collum does
not give them a number. And he is there again, climbing up Mendick
hill in the early morning stillness with sandwiches packed in an old
haversack and bottled water – plastic bottles that make the water
look blue. There with his own quiet boy this time and Collum telling
the same old stories of sheep in stone pens and cows in lamp-lit
barns, and a boy and a girl kissing up in the clouds. Collum's son
walks behind him and does not think a grandfather could ever
have been a boy. And he wonders who this girl Mary could be.

'Hair black and shiny like new-cut coal', Collum tells his son.

But the boy does not know what new-cut coal might look like.

The climb is as slow as Collum remembers. He notices this time
small yellow flowers pressed to the hill, like tiny stars against a
green dark night, and a bird hanging in the air, in the sky, making
a door-hinge squeak, over and over, the sound falling and rising
again with the movement of the bird. Near its nest they must be,
he tells his son. The boy shrugs and Collum sees himself reflected
there.

At the top of the hill Collum finds a surprise cotton-grass brackish
pool with rainbows adrift on the skin of black water, and a rough

wind combing the crest of the hill, combing it flat, spit-sticky flat, like his Da once did with his boy-hair, like he does on schooldays with his own son. And just as before, that first time he climbed the hill, Collum stands tall, the truer copy of his Da now he is grown. Holds a wet finger in the air, this time knowing to feel for the cool wind's breath at his fingertips. And in his shadow a boy like before, not knowing or understanding but doing it anyway, just the same.

Collum unscrews the cap from a glint-silver urn. He raises it high in the air, in the clouds almost, and tips out a grey ghost to chase after the first. 'Always chasing her', he thinks and in his head it is his Da's voice he hears giving shape and sound to the words.

Not so blue this day, the faraway hills a grey smear across the sky and the air chill and wet, but it feels the same somehow there on the top of Mendick hill.

'Shouldn't we say something?' says the boy – the boy now and the boy back then.

Collum shakes his head, just as his Da had, and he puts his arm around his son's shoulders. 'All we need do is listen', Collum says, and there's something like an echo when he says it.

Douglas Bruton is a writer of short stories and prose. He is widely published in literary magazines and competition anthologies. He won the Biscuit Prize in 2009 and the Hissac Short story competition in 2008 and has won some recognition from The Bridport Prize. His novel for children was published in September 2009; it is called The Chess Piece Magician.

Kýrie, Eléison

By Christy Di Frances

How it takes away your breath—this
passing glimpse of one small leaf that
starkly clings to your bare ankle,
plastered on the soaking skin. And
for the briefest moment now this
sudden strangeness (wilting fast with
autumn fire) seems a burden
far too heavy for such slender
bone and flesh.

*Christy Di Frances hails from across the Atlantic and is currently in her third
year of a PhD, examining various aspects of Robert Louis Stevenson's ideology of
adventure at the University of Aberdeen. She previously received a BA in English
from her home city of Milwaukee and an MA in Creative Writing from the
University of Adelaide in South Australia, where she thoroughly enjoyed editing
an anthology of Creative Writing for Wakefield Press.*

Pendulum
By Jane O'Neill

On a clear day she walked to the Willows
ate pink Battenberg and drank sugary tea.

But when care-worn and hollow-eyed
she shuffled along wearing lead boots.

When she was up she would talk, talk, talk
her Grand plans rocketing into space.

When it was dark outside and dark inside
under heaps of cotton, she slept and slept.

I should have known there was something wrong
when she bought the red coat:

for it clashed with her auburn hair
for it clashed with her auburn hair
for it clashed with her auburn hair

Jane O'Neill joined Esther Read's writing class at Dundee University to learn the craft of writing. Five years on, two of her short stories and a poem have been included in anthologies published by Nethergate Writers. She is currently attending Jim Stewart's Poetry Class with the aim of Thinking Poetically. Jane's stories and poems are inspired by her observation of, and interest in people.

The Would Be New Man

By S. O'Tierney

How could one person have so many intimate friends? Surely she was imagining half of them? Was she jabbering just to amuse herself? How was she so oblivious to the exasperation of her fellow travelers? Since Glasgow she had called Stacey, Julie, Donna, Kirsty, Marie... Donny lost count after that.

'Hiya! It's me, Jolene... I'm on the train... Wait till ye hear... I'm going back to Nick... He proposed!... Tonight... Aye, he kept phoning me, pure hunners of calls... Nah, I just played pure hard to get... Aye. He's meeting me at Lochross. I cannae wait...'

While the train was packed, her voice was less distinct. But the further north they traveled, the emptier the coach became and the more audible her shrieks. Now it was just the two of them in coach F, and Donny could hear every word. How could she use a train journey to tell everyone of her romance? A verbal round-robin, even more excruciating than all those smug letters he had received from old friends every Christmas since Martha left him.

He had no desire to know so much about Jolene. It made him feel

creepy, like listening Tom or something. Actually, he never cared
to know much about anyone - his indifference to gossip was eighth
on Martha's list of ten reasons for leaving him. How she'd have
loved this. He could picture Martha closing her eyes to feign sleep
and craning her neck craning in Jolene's direction. Her whole body
would tauten with concentration. He pictured how her lips would
be curling with amusement. If only he had moved to another coach
earlier. But if he went now Jolene would surely guess he was leaving
just to escape her, and although he couldn't stand hearing so much
about her personal life he had no wish to offend her. There was also
the small but distinct surprise of the dark loveliness of her eyes as
he had passed her on his way to the buffet.

If she wasn't so young he might even have fancied her. But no,
his long history of being dumped (always with heartfelt apologies)
presaged yet another rejection as the likeliest - no, the inevitable
- outcome to any attempted romance. Jolene was two seats away
on the opposite side, so he couldn't quite see her, but Donny was
so acutely conscious of her she might as well have been sat on his
lap. Reading or dozing was impossible - her chattering and giggling
were like bees in his brain.

Since Martha left him, he hadn't had any relationship that lasted
more than a month. Mary, the last one, had departed with, 'You
never even asked how I felt when my aunt died.'

It was horribly déjà vu. Martha had accused him of indifference
after her cancer scare. How could she think that? Just because he
never bawled his head off? Three days after getting the all clear,
she left him.

'If you really had been dying I'd have looked after you to the very
end.' But even as the words left his mouth Donny sensed they didn't
sound right. He had never been able to tell Martha how much she
meant to him.

By now Donny knew all about how Jolene had known Nick since
she was a child but didn't go out with him until she was twenty-
three. 'But he was such a geek!' she told friend after friend. They
broke up after a few months. 'But it was like - you know - I just like
- yeah! I just never got over him!'

Nick was a marine biologist in Kirkwall but even though he

adored Jolene and would do 'absolutely anything' for her, he
wouldn't move. He was only happy in the wilderness.

'I just always thought like no way... So yeah, two years in Newcastle
and now I'm like cured...Yeah, I've done all the bright lights. I'm
dead mature now... I'm pure sick of the rat race and all that random
false stuff, y'know?... Aye! Just had to get it out of my system... Aye,
like Nick's pure into nature, y'know? He's like pure dead spiritual,
know what I mean?'

Each friend was treated to a fulsome account of Nick's amazing
body, finished every time with, 'Guess what? His beard's away... It
used to be pure red so I cannae wait to see him without it... When
he agreed to shave his beard I pure knew I had him.'

Had Martha ever described him with such excitement to anyone?
Dream on. But Donny still remembered how she admired his hands
on their first date. Ten years later she told him that he never returned
her compliment, not then on their first date, nor ever after, though
she never stopped longing for one.

'You could have said my hair was nice. Or my eyes. Even my
dress. But oh no, Mr. Cucumber could never stoop to compliment
anyone. I was so stupid. I thought I could get you out of your shell.
I've wasted ten years of my life trying to reach you. Ten years. I
hardly know you any better now than the day we first met. Actually
I know you even less. Everything I thought I knew about you was
wrong. It was all in my imagination.'

Donny felt bewildered and accused of wrongs he had never
committed. He hated it when she called him Mr.Cucumber. What
did she expect to discover in him? He never hid anything from her.
She was smart; surely she saw on their very first date that he had
no unknown depths. Was that so terrible?

'Nick! Why wasn't your phone on?... Conferencing? Oooooh',
Jolene giggled gleefully. 'I've been ringing you all day! Ah... Oh,
cool... Aye, packed from Glasgow but it's pure empty now, just me
and this random guy somewhere, I think.'

Donny cringed.

'No! It's flown by... Catching up with me mates... I never told
anyone before today 'cos I was keeping it secret.'

Donny wondered at this.

'Snap! Me too!' Another bout of giggling. 'You booked us in as Mr. and Mrs. Duncan?' She squealed laughter like a three year old on a trampoline. 'Oh Nick, I cannae wait! You're leaving now? It'll be midnight when we get there?... You'll be at the station before me?... I'm pure dying to see you', she whispered, then smacked kisses into her phone.

Donny wanted to bury his face in his arms on the table in front of him and cry his eyes out. He used to love it when Martha blew kisses down the phone to him. It never occurred to him that she wanted him to return the kisses. She never told him that. Not until after she decided to leave him, and then like a Day of Judgment she recalled every grievance accumulated over ten years, omitting none. Donny had listened in stupefied silence. He'd have felt unbearably foolish but he really would have tried to smack kisses on the phone if only she had told him sooner how much it meant to her. Instead she left him for Dr Reid, a G.P with a mouth like a fish.

Donny had one thing in common with Jolene. He too was travelling north for a new life. He had never been to Lochross and knew nobody here, but six months ago he heard on a radio programme that this town had the highest surplus of single women in the whole country. That night he searched the internet for any available job there. Destiny seemed to be yelling at him when he read, weeks later, the vacancy for a supermarket manager, and he had every requirement asked for. He'd been in retail for over twenty years. 'But I'm good with people', he had pleaded with Martha. 'Ask any of my staff, they all say I'm the fairest manager they've ever had. Just go and ask anyone working for me how fair I am.'

'Donny', Martha replied, 'I know how fair you are. You're perfectly fair. But you couldn't comfort a kitten.'

For a while after Martha left him, Donny hoped he could win her back, it was just a matter of figuring out how to show all that emotional stuff she wanted. So he signed up for a course in the local community centre called 'Finding Your Inner Child. Men Only'. But on the first night, each of the other nine men wept as they talked about their fathers, and Donny had been totally freaked out. He was certain there was not a deeper, more suffering, self buried inside him, but in the hope of winning Martha back he would continue searching.

His next venture was a residential weekend in 'Self Appreciation and Fulfillment', run by a Californian whose website boasted thousands of testimonials to finding 'genuine euphoria' from people who had previously been living 'half a life'. But when he got to the Genuine Euphoria Centre, he found out he was the only man in a group of twenty seekers of self-appreciation and fulfillment, and promptly lost his voice for the weekend. His most recent failure was a course on 'Reach Your Inner Goal', which he abandoned after three sessions, though that was where he met Mandy.

'Nick! Hiya!...Nothin! Just wanted to hear your voice!...How far are you from the station? ...Oh Nick! I so want to be with you! ...I cannae wait! ...I'm hungry for you, Nick! ... (more thrilled laughter) ... I know you're driving... Yes... See you soooon!'

More kissing, then silence again. Except for her nails clicking on the table and her feet drumming the floor. Donny started biting his nails in sympathy - how could Martha ever have thought him unfeeling? Just because he didn't show it? But now Donny felt he understood, he had learned the hard way what women wanted. If some woman would give him just one more chance, he'd show her that he has as much sympathy, empathy (was that it?) and emotion as the next new man. Even if he felt like a prat, he'd do it. Anything was better than living alone.

'Come on, Nick, answer! ...Pick up your phone!...Answer, damn you!'

Oh God, Donny thought, three minutes since the last call. I can't bear any more kissing. Don't answer Nick. Let her wait, you'll see her in no time. Then you'll be together the rest of your lives. And I'll be alone.

Jolene was dialing again, and cursing again. Again and again, she dialed and cursed. Still Nick didn't answer. Her rising agitation was eating into Donny. He glared at his watch, willing the hands to move faster but every second felt longer than the one before it. 'This is torturing me too.' he wanted to tell Jolene, 'I'll never be so glad to have reached anywhere.'

Donny heard her gasp. Someone was on the other end of the phone. 'Sorry?' Jolene gasped more loudly. 'Gary who? What! How do you mean?' Suddenly her voice was so quiet and scared he barely heard it. 'That's pure rubbish ... But he's meeting me at the station in ten minutes!... He cannae be!... Accident?'

Donny shrank into his seat.

Suddenly the phone flew over Donny's head and hit the door ten feet away.

Her screams filled the coach. They hammered his head. His spine hurt. His hands were shaking. His kneecaps were juddering. If he edged forward Donny would see her, but he didn't dare. If Martha was here she'd run over to Jolene without thinking and hold her tightly. Martha only had to open her mouth for the right words to come out. But what could he say? 'Sorry for your trouble?' The words humiliated Donny by their inadequacy.

But he had to do it. It had to be done. He had to go over and offer the girl some comfort. It was inhuman not to. Damn! Where was the ticket collector or someone? Couldn't they hear her? Jolene was howling and slamming her hands on the table.

She's forgotten me, Donny told himself, if I approach her now I'll frighten her. And crying is supposed to be good for you.

But her grief was shredding him up inside. He'd jump out the window to escape it. There was another thirteen minutes of this. No, he could not take it. Slowly, Donny stood up. Jolene's head was in her arms, her body convulsing as she howled and sobbed. Silent and watchful as a burglar, he gathered his two suitcases and rucksack. Donny crept down the aisle away from her and she never noticed him, thank God. If there was a woman in Coach G he would tell her. Yes, that's the best idea.

O'Tierney was born in Dublin in 1960, has been writing since 1964, and has occasional publications in literary magazines. O'Tierney currently lives in Scotland and is teaching part-time.

The Talk

By Leila Webster

A word at a time
it comes
spluttered, stuttered,
twisting the tongue.
Till it staggers out drunken
reeking of sentiments,
striking its recipient
dead centre.

Leila Webster, 24, is a graduate in German and Modern History from the University of St Andrews. Originally from Devon, England, she now lives in St. Andrews with her husband, Allan.

Eleven in the Morning

By Zoe Venditozzi

Tony's Diner' was how Laurie imagined Russia pre-Gorbachev. It had it all: wood panelling, sepia effect Americana posters and the radio playing hits from the sixties. A few cheap looking Christmas decorations were scattered about and a limp Christmas tree stood in a corner with a fall of needles all around it on the floor. Nine or ten ornaments were grouped together around the upper branches and a lop-sided angel drooped over the sorry mess.

The cafe had about twenty tables, most of which were taken by a cavalcade of poor-looking locals. The table next to them held three old women with hardly a full set of teeth between them. They were taking turns feeding an ugly square-headed baby chips from their plates. It gummed the yellow pieces while making a groo noise. There was something repellent about the baby, and as it rolled its greedy looking eyes in Laurie's direction she considered telling Gerry she'd rather go elsewhere. But Gerry was smiling at the depressed waitress as she ambled over to their table and before Laurie knew it, he'd ordered them both cooked breakfasts.

Gerry and Laurie sat in silence and looked around. The walls were covered in blackboards displaying menu items. Laurie scanned fruitlessly for spelling mistakes or unnecessary apostrophes but there weren't any. Mind you, how hard was it to get egg and chips wrong? But she'd seen it done, more times than she'd cared to. The menu held all the usual suspects: pie and chips, bridie and chips, macaroni cheese and chips, sausage and chips. So many chips.

'Do beans count as vegetables?' Laurie asked Gerry.

'No, I don't think so. But there is a healthy choice on the menu if that's what you're worried about.'

Laurie laughed. 'Oh yeah, what?'

Gerry pointed to the wall above the stage-like serving area. On it was another blackboard advertising a steakwich salad roll.

'Only £2.95. Bargain!' Laurie laughed. 'What is a steakwich? And what do you think Tony's interpretation of a salad consists of?'

Gerry considered for a moment. 'Iceberg, one piece of. Two slices of tomato. One slice of cucumber. If it's a really healthy salad.'

Laurie looked around herself again. She felt like a fraud. 'God. What are we doing?'

Gerry reached across and squeezed her hand. 'Nothing much – just having a bit of breakfast, hanging about a bit.'

'Look at that guy there.' She nodded at a man in his forties or fifties – it was hard to tell – who was dressed in a camouflage jacket and trousers. He appeared to be wearing some sort of green netting around his neck as a scarf. He was reading the paper and sipping occasionally from a mug.

'Why?' asked Gerry.

'I dunno, he's just piqued my interest. He's all dressed for a war or something. Why do people wear things like that? Why wear a uniform if you aren't in the army?'

'Comfort? Preparedness?' Gerry shrugged. 'Less to think about in the morning?'

Laurie thought back to a picture she'd seen in Gerry's bedroom showing him in Army uniform.

'Were you in the army for long?'

'A bit, yeah.' He frowned down at the formica table top. She knew he didn't want to talk about it.

'Why did you leave? Why did you join?' She laughed but Gerry wasn't amused. He picked at the cuticles on his left thumb with his left index finger and shrugged.

'Steady job. I didn't know what else to do.' But he could have done anything. Just about. But some sort of fantasy about being a man had interested him. He'd seen himself as some sort of humble hero – a saver of women and children, who'd remember him forever. Maybe this guy had the same fantasies.

The waitress approached their table carrying two steaming plates. She was wearing a badge that read, 'I've been kissing Santa Claus'.

'Here ye are,' she said, putting the plates down firmly on the formica. Suddenly she smiled moonily at Gerry. 'Would you like any sauce?'

'No thanks,' said Laurie, but the waitress only had eyes for Gerry. She smiled at him again.

'Tomato please.'

'Coming right up,' said the waitress and bounded off to the kitchen.

'You've an admirer!' Laurie was inexplicably irritated.

'I seem to bring it out in older ladies.'

'So you do!' said Laurie, thinking of Gerry's neighbour and the barmaid in the pub. 'Maybe they want to mother you. I can understand that,' she smiled at Gerry, then glanced away, embarrassed.

'Come on,' Gerry picked up his fork and waved it over her fry up. 'Tuck in, before it gets cold.'

The food was piled up on the plate shining greasily under the strip lights. She poked the yolk of the egg with her fork and took a deep breath. No, not the egg first. She speared the piece of lone sausage which resembled a cross section of brain, ready to be examined. She put it down again, scraping it off her fork with the side of the plate. There were some cold-looking beans, half a dozen pensioner-grey mushrooms, a shrivelled piece of half burnt bacon and two pieces of fried bread which looked to be more oil than bread.

'What's wrong? Not hungry?' asked Gerry, a laden fork half way up to his mouth. His lips had a shimmery layer of grease on them and Laurie imagined herself kissing him and looked away quickly.

She shrugged. She could feel her jaw tightening up and her tongue lying dully against the bottom of her mouth. She couldn't think of a single thing to say, or rather, she could think of several polite, acceptable things to say but knew she wouldn't be able to force the words out. She cast around the room looking for a distraction. She could feel her throat closing in on itself and her stomach shrivelling down to nothing. Of course, everywhere she looked she could see food. The old lady sitting behind them was cutting up egg and chips for her Down syndrome son. She looked up at Laurie and gave her a big, gappy smile and still Laurie couldn't force herself to get it together. God, if that woman could do it, why couldn't she?

What did she have to complain about? She was perfectly healthy, had a job, somewhere to live, a boyfriend, and another man interested. And what was she doing? Hanging about in a shitty cafe feeling sorry for herself. Pathetic. Her eyes filled up with tears and she felt like punching herself in the face.

Gerry started to reach across the table to her but she moved her hand quickly away and looked over his shoulder to the window. It was grey outside and looked like it might rain. Typical. Why didn't they get snow anymore? It was only a week until Christmas, but it felt more like November. Nothing was how it was supposed to be.

Eleven in the Morning is a chapter of Zoe Venditozzi's most recent novel, Anywhere Else but Here, which has been longlisted for the 2010 Dundee International Book Prize. Zoe has had both poetry and prose published in various national and international publications and is very active in the Dundee literary community.

Elisa Segrave's Diary
By Elisa Segrave

S unday

`Ha! It's hilarious how you're frightened of your daughter!'

`she v strict!'

`WHO IS THE BEARDED MAN IN MY SPARE ROOM SMOKING? THIS IS NOT ON.'

`Apologies. Went out to supper w Mark and Jen they missed last train home. Assure you no smoking. Sheets in machine now. Your daughter furious - v. frightening!'

`Would a latish lunch work?'

`I will be at a credit crunch drinks party till 1.30. Do u want to *come in there or better not? Otherwise come here 1.30.'*

`Great!`

`P. *change time visit today. Am putty in his hands! (at least not change day of meeting, unlike your girlfriend!)'*

`Pse *bring newspaper, my lodger has interviewed Craig Brown who has been sacked'.*

`1 *30ish at your house'*

`ok *will be 2 ish'*

`Good *as am trying sober up eating 2 boiled eggs'.*

`Ha! *When P. coming? You must remain cool'.*

`Now. *Trying sober up after champagne credit crunch party eating 2 boiled eggs. Will tell my daughter if P. two-timing me.'*

Later: `Yes it all makes sense! Thrilled u back on P. – he's a proper man. My girlfriend ill again. Seeing someone else tonight.'

These are the various texts that went back and forth from and to my mobile today. Before I went to the credit crunch drinks party starting at 12, I got a call from my daughter in London saying that a bearded man and a girl were in the spare room in my flat – my daughter's old bedroom. (She'd left her mobile charger there and had gone in to retrieve it and found a couple in bed there.) She also said there was a strong smell of smoke. Naturally, I sent the above message in capitals to Tim my – lodger. I knew he was staying overnight Saturday, after finishing work at the newspaper, instead of going to his father's in Oxford as he often does. Tim later texted back that the `couple' were his friends, Mark and Jen, who had missed their last train home. Tim denied there'd been any smoking in the bedroom.

A nerve-wracking time yesterday, Saturday, regarding my affair
with P. I went over to lunch with the Partridges, a couple I don't
know that well. It was pouring with rain, and outside the Catholic
church – where I used to go some Sundays with my father, halfway
to the Partridges – there were bad floods. Earlier, I had received
a text from P. saying: 'Fell off bike in rain. C u tea tomorrow?' I
texted back: 'Are u injured? Yes what time?' I then received the
following text: 'No 4 ish?' I texted back: 'Fine'. Though ten days ago
he'd said he was coming for dinner that day.

Anyway, I got to the Partridges just after 1. I apologised for my
clothes, I was wearing some outsize joggers, but said I was going to
have to exercise my dog after lunch in the rain. I then went next
door to find P. standing by the fireplace! He seemed pleased to
see me, and I nearly blurted out that if I'd known he'd be there I
wouldn't have worn joggers. He said he'd been dropping some money
over to a freelance gardener and had called on the Partridges, then
stayed on when he'd heard I was coming for lunch. He asked why
I was wearing joggers. I explained that my son was very keen on
economising and often gave me presents, such as these joggers from
charity shops. Also, it was raining and I would have to exercise my
dog in the rain.

I pretended to have heard from another source about his fall
from the bike. P. then confirmed he had not been hurt nor the bike
damaged. (A couple of summers ago, my ex boyfriend Hal had
fallen off his motor bike when he was over from Paris, and I'd had
to take him to Casualty on a Saturday. We'd waited for hours, and
I'd missed the men's Wimbledon Finals.)

After lunch, P. left and I went for a wet walk with Mrs Partridge
and my dog. He uncharacteristically chased a sheep, and they all
ran except for one who fell over and then seemed a bit confused.
Mrs P. went and righted the sheep, saying it was alright. It was
slow to rejoin the flock. I guardedly asked Mrs P. a bit about P's
marriage. Mrs P. said that P. had driven thirty minutes from his
house before lunch to give cash to the woman freelance gardener
who had a 'come hither' manner, and that P. had then asked the
Partridges about the state of the gardener's marriage! I said grimly
that P. was a philanderer and always had been.

Naturally, I was secretly very thrown to hear this about the gardener and devastated to think that he might be two-timing me with her - and two-timing his wife with me and her!) I rang Tim – who is the only person apart from my daughter who knows about my affair with P. – to get counselling. I am a fool to have embarked on an affair with a married man.

I felt rather tearful about P. that evening, while alone, but supposed it was my own fault.

I later cheered up after reading an article about Castro, and I sent P. a text saying I wanted to go to Cuba and did he want to come. He texted back: 'Is it a night club?'

He came over at 2 the following day, Sunday, and I very much enjoyed seeing him. I said later: "Mrs Partridge said you were after the gardener." He seemed amused.

Tuesday

Coffee with my old friend Miranda who is a compulsive helper. She'd said she could come only if she had already had a call about her sick mother, then she might have to leave early to take lunch to someone who's had his toe removed. I said dismissively: 'Oh everyone I know is dying or ill! I'm off to visit a woman of only 45 who's had two new hips; her boyfriend's left her, and she had her breast off two months ago!' This silenced her.

Elisa Segrave went to Edinburgh University to study English and Philosophy but 'dropped out' after one year, to work in a hospital linen room then in an office in Hanover Square, New York City. She published her first book The Diary of a Breast (Faber) in 1995, after getting divorced and breast cancer. Elisa spends much of her time writing her own diary of which there are many volumes. Elisa says: 'I must write my diary or I feel I will go mad. [...] The diary is my master and I am its slave. I cannot escape from its tyranny.'

The Secret of My Successes, or, Why I Don't Want You Any More

By Nicole Devarenne

Freecycle Offer:

Sony Hi Fi with 5 disc CD player twin cassette, no speakers
Pine Bread Bin
Assorted Country and Western cassette tapes
Assorted records and singles
Pine Double Bed frame (one fixing missing)
Woman's brown leather jacket (medium, size 14)
Table lamp made from wooden snooker
Light Wave battery operated optical art
Large Blue plastic fruit bowl and colander
Boxed "Brit Quiz" and "Atmosfear", Pub Quiz 60s & 80S Pop board games
Large Lilac Cuddly rabbit
Bag of assorted Chef clothing
2 car cassette players

Available for uplift ASAP

'Who needs to play seven albums at the same time anyway,' he said
when his dog mistook the speakers for a fire hydrant.

My mother used to hide her money in the bread bin, on the principle
that no one would ever think to look for it there. Guess she didn't
expect a burglar trained in metaphor.

Even as a child, I should have known better than to sing along with
words that went 'if I could move I'd get my gun and put her in the
ground'.

The only thing he took with him was the record player. The least he
could have done was to also take the Bat out of Hell.

Funny what happens to a bed without all the legs attached.

My whole life I've wanted to be a size eight. That's, like, half the
size I really am. I was maybe an eight when I was eleven. Eleven
was when I started wanting a leather jacket. So eventually I decided
I was never going to be a size eight, and I bought a leather jacket.
Then I got a tapeworm and now I'm a size eight. So you can imagine.

I married this guy who, every time he saw an item in the Salvation
Army store, said 'With a pair of wire cutters and a light bulb I
could turn that into something classy.'

The bad days are the ones when you try to find other words than
the ones on the box and it doesn't make a damned bit of difference.

Eventually I realised that if a colour doesn't occur naturally in nature,
it's going to look kind of odd holding a colour that does.

Maybe nobody besides me even remembers what people sang and
wore and watched in the 60s. Maybe nobody besides me finds the

80s sexy any more.

Say what you like, it's just no substitute for chicken.

The second guy I married on account of he smelled like bacon, and I was tired of cooking.

When they stole my car they left the cassette player lying in the driveway. With the insurance money I bought a cheaper car and a more expensive cassette player. Damned if those shitheads didn't come back again.

Nicole Devarenne teaches English Literature and Film Studies at the University of Dundee. She grew up in South Africa and the U.S.A. and is still finding her accent and voice. This found-object piece was written as a response to a writing group exercise.

Hourglass

By Jacqueline Thompson

I look better in mirrors, she thinks.
It's something in the flip of my features,
something in the tilt of the glass.

'Move the pin up a notch, tight,
as tight as that, that's right,
so tight the leather squeaks.'

'I could wrap one hand round that waist.
I could put gold round that finger,
tie you up tight like a gift.'

Before breakfast my stomach is flat,
she aches, it swells as the hours slide.
I'll buy tights that suck it back,
hold me in close like a hug.
'You won't wear heels tonight,
I like you yards below,
I like your eyes looking up.
I tell you when your roots grow black.'

There is hell in the hourglass, she knows,
it drains away too quick, cuts me to the quick.
When the roots run to grey it will end.

I sleep wearing make-up.
He's never seen my face,
I set my alarm early.

'Nearly there', a swig of black wine,
hands encircling an intestinal pang.
'...you're nearly there, you know.'

'Just one more notch',
hot breath on the neck,
'and you're perfect.'

Jacqueline Thompson was born in Arbroath and graduated from Dundee University in 2009 where she is now studying for an MLitt in Creative Writing. She has had her work in New Writing Dundee 2009, For A' That (a Dundee University Press anthology celebrating Burns), and recently featured as 'Poem of the Month' in The Scotsman.

Empire
By Albert Lehzen

S he is obsessed with Empire.

Locked in the contours of her naked back, I pull my hands along her stomach. Her eyes are looking down, so that they appear closed. Her skin is warm and I can feel her heart beneath her breast. She breathes slowly.

Rolling over on to her side, dragging her fingers up the inside of my thigh, I involuntarily respond by folding like a jack knife. I pull her close to my chest. Eyes locked, we gaze into the pattern and shade of the iris.

'When you die, I will wear only black.' Her voice breaks the silence, and I smile as response to her utterance.

'When do you ever wear any other colour?' Her eyes smile at me, but her mouth does not snap or twist into laughter. 'We are not amused,' is her reply.

*

We are sitting together in the bedroom. I recline on the bed, while she sits at a large vanity desk. She applies make-up, tracing the shape of her eyelids in black, pulling her eyes to opposite points, a small black line. I look at her body from behind: she can not see my gaze. Wearing a black corset constructed of heavy linen and steel boning, she trains her waist. Like an awkward hourglass she perches on a small piano stool. Her shoulders taper down to her waist, sixteen inches, and then her body explodes out again with the appearance of her hips. Turning her head, she looks at me.

On the mirror behind her, she has stuck three pictures beneath the wooden frame. Victoria as we know her, the queen of the world's greatest Empire, looks out at me with her round face and pointed nose — taken after the death of Albert, she mourns. To the left of Victoria, Lauren Bacall lounges against a wall, her full lips and wide cheeks smiling. The third and final picture is of me, oddly enough. My face is awkward, it is uneven. I remember reading somewhere that people are attracted to symmetry. My face is unattractive and intruding against the reflective surface, my photo appears ridiculous, I appear ridiculous: I will remove it later.

Coquettishly she looks at me; her hair is combed into large spherical collections. It is ace of spades black and it frames her angular face.

'Did you know that the Prince Albert is supposedly named after Victoria's husband? He was rumoured to have one.' She whispers slightly. Honestly I didn't know that, but I don't believe it either. Her obsession escapes through her eyes, and I can read her thoughts.

'Would you get one? A Prince Albert, I mean.' She teases.

I scoff at her. 'My dick creeps me out enough as it is.'

She looks genuinely heart broken.

'Well, Victorian women apparently were among the first to get nipple piercings, To increase sexual pleasure.' She runs her tongue against her top row of teeth then rudely sticks it out at me.

*

I move my hand up, towards her head, to stroke her face. On the way, my watch tugs on her nipple ring. She squeals, then laughs.

'You will not believe how many things that ring has been caught on!' Erect, her nipple looks unusual as the metallic bar forces its presence beneath the soft, tender tissue.

I like it; it gives her an erotic edge; power – a power to control herself. The silver ring, like a small detonator on a flesh coloured explosive.

Sliding down the bed, I place my hand on her thigh; I encompass her knee in my outstretched fingers and apply light pressure on the soft flesh behind her knee cap. Stroking my hair with her fingers, she lies back and stretches her toes. I catch the pungent stench of adrenaline in my chest and tackle it wilfully, as my fingers continue to travel.

She breaks the silence, 'Ladies, lie back and think of England!' I laugh and feel awkward with my fingers hovering intimately; I sigh and lie back down beside her.

*

It is January and it is cold. Not only cold, it is windy too. I am in awe as she walks alongside me. She is wearing a Victoriana inspired ensemble.

'The shirt is based on the Victorian tradition of tailored lines.' She makes her clothes herself, and she is rather successful at it. 'I use black lace on white cotton to add emphasis. I am reading Dracula, and just now Lucy is wearing a scarf to hide her vampire bite marks, I thought it would be rather quaint to copy this.'

She lifts the scarf to reveal that she has no scars on her throat. 'I know the puff ball skirt is not strictly Victorian, but I like this one, although it annoys me. I like the way it gives me this real feminine shape...' She puts her hands around her waist. Her hands pressed against a leather corset beneath, the material of her shirt makes her hands slip down to her hips. '...but I don't like it in black. In poor lighting it just looks like a screwed up mess. Latex tights. Definitely not Victorian. But very shiny, and that works for me. Look at my ankles in these things. And check it out...' She pauses for effect. '...and these shoes I bought from eBay. The seller told me they are actually Victorian, but I would guess Edwardian or certainly pre world war one...'

She thinks silently, then questions.

'They are old, and they do set the look off. What do you think?'

In her appearance there is no fault. And her attention to detail and influences are inspired, but what I think doesn't matter.

*

Conquered, I lay in the silence of morning. My naked torso is cold and, as she places each metallic disc upon my skin, I shudder.

'Eighteen-seventy-five,' she whispers, placing the final bronze disc onto my chest. 'Look,' she directs, as she forces the coin into my view. 'It has an impression of young Victoria, it's a bit damaged. Yet reliable Minerva on the front still sits steady: her Britannia shield, a little bit marked— but that doesn't matter, it's the history that counts...' She continues to speak, constructing a verbal inventory of her bountiful collection. I smile and nod my head, trapped beneath her body as she talks.

I can feel the euphoric shadow of Empire; her irrefutable dominance to which I wilfully surrender.

She makes an empty remark about Victorians and Freud; I laugh anyway.

My chest expands under the bronze discs, soldiers procuring control, adopting and illustrating the cartography of my skin; domineering.

As I muse, her wandering finger trembles over my chest, and I smile as I experience the first string snapping against the bow of my heart: a piercing and resolute soprano which, so high, only I hear it echoing within my ears. She removes the coins with care and takes them away. I look at her forehead as she returns and try to ignore the feeling of distinction which has sparked in my mind: of kings beneath queens, and of me alongside her. Empire, I laugh.

*

I am in a room with her. She is surrounded by friends, all of whom dress like her and feign some interest or other in the eccentric fashions of history. That sickly taste of epiphany poisons my lips as I smirk.

I wonder if this is what she thinks Empire is really about, saving face, and keeping up appearances with the mob. Her waist is not trained for her, or even for me; it is to be presented to this society of peers. I have to laugh as I realise it is not Empire which she tries to encapsulate, but rather her majesty Victoria, and her society of Victorians.

Ignoring the smudged face of vanity to my side – speaking profusely on the invention of the first computer and 'Ada Lovelace, what a cool name Lovelace, of the Manor house' – I drift into deep contemplation.

Queen Victoria had once ruled an Empire from seclusion, too melancholic to face society. Her life dedicated to her beloved Albert, she lived as he would have, and died after losing her sight and her reason – a complete loss of power. I stumble on the footnote of my thought process. Victoria's Empire is suddenly surmised in my mind, a corseted society built on image and personal opinion, a society that finally surpassed her; she had lost it all. Her personal Empire had fallen. My obsession escapes through my eyes as I smile. Her Empire.

I find it difficult to imagine the woman I love, in the corner reclining against a china filled cabinet, knowing any of this information; a tragic history of negation and reversal, of having all, then nothing at all. I think hard.

Offence enters my bloodstream as I think of Empire, of the power, and of the control. The conceit to abuse another into submission.

Of one beneath the other. Of coercion and force.

And of her.

*

Ajar, the door frames her sitting on the edge of the bed. In her hands she holds a small ornate compact mirror; applying porcelain powder to her cheeks, she smiles for no one. I shy away from the door as she looks into the mirror: I try to hide from her. Watching, captivated, I slow my breathing to a heavy ululation.

'When you die, I shall wear only black,' she repeats, smiling into the shallow glass. Again, she repeats the phrase, forming her syllables harshly, like currency being pressed between a patterned die. I move behind the door, creeping, invading her privacy. I watch between the hinge and the doorframe: convinced.

Standing, she continues to look into the compact, pouting her large lips and smiling without passion. Her naked body is a white mark against a dark shadow. Walking across the small space of our bedroom, she approaches the vanity desk, where her reflection catches and lingers. On the surface of the table, surrounded by her memora

bilia, ephemera, stands a new and solitary golden picture frame.
Within it my face grins childishly. My other eyes, my photographed
eyes, catch her line of sight. In a simple gesture she challenges the
system, overthrows democracy. A slow and simple movement, majestic,
charming and equally hideous, she pushes the frame onto its front.
The plastic resonates against the table. It falls.

I feel it now, the confirmation of power. A heavy dread. She continues
to smile in the mirror, posing, contorting her body; and smiling.

We battle in silence, control slipping between our mindless fingers.
She tries to sit, however her seat is obstructed; on the piano stool's
dull upholstery sits a small hardback, an old Queen Victoria biography.
Outstretching her fingers she swats it from the seat onto the floor.
Nonchalantly she begins to apply her makeup as I turn away. As
if aware of my presence, she turns and looks at the open door. As
I blink, I glimpse her silhouette; a long forehead, wide cheeks and
a pointed nose. Behind her, against the mirror, her döppelganger
smiles with unease.

*

We sit together beneath a blinding sun.Her fingers latched between
mine. I innocently prod; irritate an argument with politic discussion.

'Would you live your life with my morals? Could you live as I dictate,
as I lived?'

'Is that a marriage proposal?' She laughs. 'If you are trying to
compare me to Victoria again, you can stop. 'Cause honestly, no, I
wouldn't live as you do.' She is not offensive, yet her lips curl with a
self-conscious appeal.

'What,' I mock appal, 'do you mean by that?'

'I please others, before myself, I have to be seen, I have to make
an impression.' She looks into the sky.

'Is my attention not enough?' I laugh.

'You are one of many, life is a greater captive audience than thou,'
she jokingly reproaches, getting to her feet.

'I'm heartbroken,' I announce, trying to hide the fact.

'That's Empire, baby,' she mocks, as she genuflects, reaching to
place a finger against my lips. I move away from her touch, the tension
of anger blistering my tongue.

*

It is dark as I finish my condemnation.

She sits on the edge of the bed; I can feel her sobbing as the mattress slowly shakes. The ruler of the relationship, of the manipulation of desire and control, has fallen; and with her, Empire tumbles steadily after covering her body in pity and shame.

I have challenged her; I opened her eyes to her idiocy and errors. I pulled at the artificial seams of her obsession, to reveal what lay beneath. Nothing. Of the books I owned she had never read them, her interest was aesthetic and shallow. I confused her mind, I asked her questions, insulted her intelligence.

All the reasons for which I love her.

As I had talked to her, like a sadist with a camera, I observed every minute twist in her face, the movement of her arms. I noticed it all, watched it all and witnessed her descent from power.

Silence pollutes the air around us; it slowly forms condensation on her eyes. Dawn steals in through the open blinds and catches on various objects cluttered around the room. Light perches on the metal of her piercing, it catches the reflection of the mirror and, somewhere on the floor, the light illuminates her collection of coins.

She sits upright as I mention her name. Crossing her arms and sighing deeply, she gazes at me from behind her shoulder. The shadow cast on her skin gives her a luminous glow which frames her silhouette in the darkness.

A line pulled taught between us, I feel the smile straighten on my lips.

Many claim that Albert Lehzen is more than just a writer: also an artist, performer and creator. At a young age, he reached notoriety with the performance piece, 'Man eating cat food in a London warehouse.' His profanity-coach, Ada Lovelace, has recently published her correspondence with Albert, Letters from a Molehill. In the preface to this publication she reminisces about her tutee, 'I used to get holographic postcards in the electropost from him, talking about his experiences as master of the intergalactic circus.' She refers to Albert's previous career in the Mechanics of Vaudeville, where he often trained robo-tigers and shagged mechanical clownettes. Albert is retired, but, despite his considerable age, he continues to wear pantaloons on a cold day. Ada ends her collection of letters on this note, 'Albert is dead downstairs, except when it comes to his one true love, Victoria. Most of the women in his life, and many men, have never been able to come to terms with this, stalking him into seclusion. Unfortunately, the world will never witness "Man eating cat food in a London warehouse, the sequel."'

Origami

By Gillian Craig

Origamic love:
like a new couple folding
a mutual sheet.

Each one's instinctive
personal moves mar final
flawless symmetry.

A crease once folded
along predetermined lines
cannot be unmade;

Souls, sheets and paper
will always bear witness to
the trace of past moves.

Gillian Craig is from Scotland, but she has spent the last ten years living in Thailand, Taiwan, Oman and Japan teaching English as a foreign language. She currently lives in Hanoi, Vietnam, where she tries to spend more time writing than she does teaching. She studied English Language at Edinburgh University, and her interests include reading, travelling, and language in all its forms. This is her second published piece of poetry.

The Owlatorium and the Cat-King

By Kirsty Logan

I met this Colombian girl, maybe three years ago now. We met in the park – the owl sanctuary. The Owlery. Owlatorium? Whatever.

The point is that it was a big mesh box and it was full of birds all screeching and flapping, and she was standing in front of it eye-to-eye with the biggest owl I'd ever seen.

'Last year,' she said without breaking eye contact, 'the roof of this cage collapsed.'

'Sweet,' I said, thinking about all those birds finally being free. Spreading their wings like they're meant to. Up up up like Icarus but never falling because this is the Northern Hemisphere and the sun is never hot enough to melt anything.

'No!' She slammed her palm against the mesh. The owl looked startled but then owls always looks startled, all birds do I suppose because they have no eyelids. Or maybe that's lizards.

Anyway, 'No!' she shouted, and even if the owl wasn't startled I sure was. She was still staring at the owl, even though it was pissed at her outburst and had turned away from her.

'They all died, she said. The roof collapsed onto them and they all died.'

Not like Icarus then, not at all, not soaring and free but mangled and twitching, a chaos of blood and feathers.

'Oh,' I said, because what else was there to say? I could say sorry but I wasn't really, not for a bunch of owls I'd never seen and never would see, and even if I had then they'd look just like the owls in this owlatorium to me, how the hell am I supposed to tell them apart?

'That sucks,' I said, because although this wasn't really a conversation I wanted it to keep going, because I'd noticed by then that she had all this glossy black hair and her face was really pretty when she wasn't scrunching it up to stare at owls.

Anyway, while I was thinking about her hair she had clearly been thinking about how dumb my comments were, because she was looking at me with this expression of disdain, literally looking down her nose at me even though I was taller by about three inches, and somehow she even looked pretty doing that.

'So listen,' I said, just for something to say, because if I gawped at her any longer she'd think I was brain-damaged or something, 'are you busy right now, because I...'

'I need a drink,' she said, and she stopped looking at the owl and she stopped looking at me and she walked away, these super-quick steps like she was about to trip over, and all I could do was follow her.

I tried to think of something clever to say, but she was wearing these backless sandals and every time she took a step I could see the white flashes of her soles, five shades lighter than the rest of her skin, and all I could think of was the flash of a rabbit's tail as it runs away, and I was too busy chasing the rabbit to think straight.

'But sometimes they get free,' she was saying, and I don't know if she'd been talking the whole time and I hadn't heard or she'd just started mid-sentence. Both seemed equally likely. I skipped a bit to try to catch up to her, and I was still staring at the length of her hair, black and shiny like a wet leech.

'Is that right,' I said, even though I didn't really know what she was talking about.

'Not that they'd understand, but when the swallows managed it,' she said, so I guess it didn't really matter whether I was listening or not, and my stride broke when I realised that maybe she hadn't meant for me to follow, maybe she wasn't talking to me at all.

She must have heard my lack of step because she turned around and held out her hand and took mine and pulled me along beside her, all in one motion like a bird opening its wings.

I don't know why I thought that we were going to a bar in the park, because it doesn't really make sense that a park would have a bar, but then I guess it makes just as much sense for a park to have an ice-skating rink or a chapel, and they do sometimes have those things.

She held my hand all the way out of the owlatorium, even though the guard at the gate stared at us like maybe I needed an escort or one of us had special needs or something, because I guess it wasn't really clear which one of us was leading the other.

'Buena suerte,' she called over her shoulder in this sing-song voice, and I guess she was saying goodbye to the owls even though they obviously couldn't hear us because they were miles away now and I bet they didn't understand Spanish anyway. She gripped my hand so tight that I could feel it slipping on the sweat of my palms.

It didn't seem like she was leading me so I led her, and I didn't know where else to take her so I took her to where I had been planning to go after I'd looked at the owls, and that was to feed the cats.

I'd been feeding the cats for a few months now, ever since I went to the park one sunny-ish day to eat my lunch. Days are only ever sunny-ish when you live in the North, never proper blazing burn-your-scalp hot like on holiday; but even sunny-ish weather brings everyone in the whole city outside. That meant the park was packed with ball-kicking kids and grande-latte office workers and hung-over students, and that meant I had to go right into the compost-smelling middle to get some space to myself. I was finishing off my sandwiches when the cats appeared. Not one by one but all at once, so that when I looked up there were dozens of them, wiping their furry sides against the legs of the bench and staring at me with big shiny eyes. I still had a bun from the baker's, so I split it into as many pieces as I could and threw it down for the cats, watching them pick the sugared chunks of dough up with their little pink tongues and their little white teeth. They prowled around me, climbing up and perching on my legs and shoulders, digging their claws into the fabric. I am the Cat-King, I thought to myself. Then I said it aloud, 'Cat-King', then louder, 'CAT-KING', and the cats joined in with their yowls and purrs and after that I went back every lunchtime even when it wasn't sunny-ish just so I could feed the cats and be their king.

She was still holding my hand, though her grip was loosening a bit as we went further into the park and the air started to smell like compost, because maybe she thought I was going to take her somewhere deserted and murder her and bury her under a bush. I knew if I gripped her hand harder she'd get freaked out but if I let it go I'd never be able to take it again, and suddenly I didn't want her to know about the cats and about me being their King.

I should have just let her go then, just walked away and remembered her forever as this crazy owl-girl who came along and distracted me for an afternoon, but that felt like giving up, and I thought maybe it could have worked. I always think that maybe it will work with crazy girls even though of course it never does.

So instead I kept my hand in hers and we kept walking, but I steered her away from the compost-smelling land of the Cat-King, and up to the south side of the park where there's a hill hiding the coastline, up to the sky so she could be closer to the birds. I was losing the rhythm of my breaths by the time we got to the top of the hill, and I could see that her feet were slipping around a lot in her sandals. I imagined the sweat on her soles tasted like clean and earthy, like grass and salt and dirt.

She stood there on the top of the hill, like this was where she'd wanted to go all along, and she looked around like she was Helen watching cities burn in her name. I knew she wanted me to say something profound, but at the time I guess I thought it was more profound not to say anything at all. I stood as close to her as I dared, and I pretended that I was watching cities burn too. After a while she sighed and shifted her feet, and started to look like she was about to say goodbye, like she was about to walk away from me and never see me again and it would be like we had never even met.

'We should sail away,' I said. 'We can get a boat and sail across the bay.' I reached into my pocket and pulled out a five-pound note, to show that I could get her a ticket for the passenger ferry. For a minute it seemed like she was considering it, because she stopped doing her cities-burning face and instead she looked down to the bottom of the hill, where the ferry ticket office sat on a patch of yellowing turf. Finally, for the first time since meeting her, I knew what to do next. I put my arms around her and I kissed her and we fell.

We were spinning, heels over hearts, and we had nothing in common and it would never work and we barely even lived in the same world but we sure could fall together. We could fall better than anyone.

We stopped, our heads throbbing and our jeans smudged brown-green with grass stains, and she looked at me. From her look I could tell that it didn't matter how good we could fall, she was never going to sail away with me.

'Sorry,' I said, and I put the five-pound note back in my pocket. She walked away, her heels flashing like rabbits' tails.

Kirsty Logan is a writer, editor, teacher, reviewer, waitress, and general layabout. She is currently working on her first novel, Little Dead Boys, *thanks to a New Writers Award from the Scottish Book Trust. Her short fiction and poetry appears in PANK, Popshot, Polluto, and some other places that don't begin with P. She likes bad horror films and sticking pins in maps. She lives in Glasgow with her girlfriend. Get in touch at kirstylogan.com.*

Six Beers and a Dog
By Diane Payne

L ook at that idiot. Now he's got a dog out in the yard.' Fred takes another swig of his beer, then looks to see why his wife isn't responding. Paula's inside the house, avoiding him. Fred repeats the comment about the dog, but yells it so she'll hear him through the open windows. He hopes his neighbor hears him also.

Ever since Fred got laid off from the factory, he spends most of his day sitting on the deck drinking beer. Doesn't matter that it's cold, forty-five degrees. He wears a stocking cap, his gloves, and an old coat and parks himself in the lawn chair.

Paula thought she heard a dog barking during the night, but that's fairly common. This dog just sounded close to her bedroom window. At first she thought she was dreaming.

Paula hears Fred laughing, a rarity these days. 'Get out here, Paula. You gotta see this!' he yells. Paula steps outside, curious about this change in mood. 'Watch that idiot picking up the dog's shit. It is hilarious. He's dry heaving!'

Bill, the neighbor, uses a scoop that's intended for cat litter. He squats above a pile of poop, scoops it, and starts gagging. Paula can't help but laugh. She hopes Bill doesn't hear them. Even the dog seems to be laughing.

Fred's on his third beer. On a good day, the third beer can get him feeling more loquacious, more friendly. That changes dramatically by the fifth beer. By the sixth beer, he'll be maudlin or angry. Rarely any surprises.

'Whose mutt is that?' Fred yells over the fence.

Scoop in one hand, plastic bag in the other, Bill notices dog shit on his fingers and starts heaving again. 'It's mine,' he yells back before turning on the hose to rinse off his hands.

'Looks like the dog has a healthy appetite.' Fred thinks he's hilarious. Paula knows this is just the beginning. Once he gets going, he's hard to stop. 'Ever have a dog before?'

Bill regrets coming outside while Fred is in his yard, but since he's been laid off, he's always outside. 'Not since I was a kid.'

'Hell, compared to me, you are still a kid. What are you? Twenty-four?'

'Close enough,' Bill mutters back.

'Where did you get that dog?'

'A friend from work was moving. She said she couldn't take the dog.'

'Ah, so you took the dog? She better be a babe for taking on this mutt. Let me guess. She'll visit her sweet dog at your house.'

Bill wishes that were the case. He met Liz at the beginning of the school year when she started providing speech therapy services at his school. Oddly enough, he'd end up stuttering whenever he talked to her. She'd laugh. He wondered if she laughed at the kids when they stuttered or just at him. He suggested that they go out for dinner, see a movie, and she always remained noncommittal, say she'd give him a call if she wasn't busy. She might as well have said, 'Drop dead.' The most he ever talked with her was when she said she needed someone to adopt this dog. He thought she had just found it, but she'd had him all year. She wanted to move into a new apartment with a pool and exercise room, but dogs weren't allowed. She brought a picture of the dog to work and posted it on the bulletin

board in the lounge. When Bill said he could keep the dog, she
didn't laugh when he stuttered. She didn't even offer to bring the
dog to his house. Instead she gave him directions to her duplex. He
was to collect the dog. His first invite to her house. And probably
his last invite.

Scooping up the poop, he knows it's unlikely she'll come to visit
the dog. She grabbed the dog's bed, his leftover food, and shoved
him out the door and into Bill's car.

'You'll love her,' she said. 'She's a great dog.'

'What's her name?'

'Bessie. And don't worry, she's been spayed and has had all her
shots. She's ready to go. She's in perfect health.'

Bessie jumped into the backseat and watched Liz through the
window as he drove off.

Tired of being ignored, Fred yells back, 'She tell you her dog was
a real shitter?'

'No, Fred, she didn't tell me that. She didn't tell me much about
this dog.'

Fred cracked up, thrilled that Bill was so obviously miserable.

'You think she'll ever come visit the mutt?'

'I doubt it, Fred.'

'Oh well, if you can't get the woman, I guess getting the mutt
is the next best thing.' He laughs hysterically, gulping down his
fourth beer. 'One bitch or another. What difference does it make?'
Paula sees his mood darken and returns to the house.

'Want a beer?' Fred offers. 'Come on over here,' he yells.

Bill doesn't want a beer but accepts it anyway. It's the same
way he felt driving off with the dog. He opens the gate and goes to
Fred's yard. Bessie follows. It's way too cold to be sitting outside
drinking a beer.

'Hey, mutt,' Fred laughs. 'Don't be shitting in my yard. You
looked like you were gonna puke picking that shit up.'

Bill nods his head in agreement, drinks his beer, and says, 'It's
been awhile since I've been around a dog.'

'You got duped into this dog, didn't you? You wanted the woman
but got the mutt. Maybe you got lucky. This ugly mutt may prove to
be the better companion.'

Bessie runs around the yard, checking out all the scents. Neither
man says anything. Bessie starts digging and Bill yells for her to
stop. She returns with the remains of a large bone.

'I'll be damned,' Fred says. 'That was Hunter's bone. Best dog I
ever had.'

Bill has lived next door for a year and there's never been a dog, so
he figures it was before his arrival.

'That beagle could hunt. Damn, he was a rare dog. Had him
twelve years. After he died, I told my wife there'd be no more dogs.
Can't after losing a dog like that. Can't.' He opened his sixth beer.

Bill nods his head in agreement.

'You don't know a good dog until you've had a dog like Hunter.'

Bill wishes he could finish his beer quicker and get home.

'Yeah,' he sighs.

Bessie sees a squirrel and chases it up a tree. She barks frantically.
Bill calls her to stop but she ignores him.

'Looks like that mutt has some hound in her. Look at her go after
that squirrel. She's halfway up that damn tree.' Fred starts bawling.
'Oh hell,' he sobs.

'Some asshole shot my Hunter. Said he was sorry. What kind of
asshole shoots someone's dog while they're hunting? She didn't die
from his bullet. She died from mine. I could tell she wouldn't make
it until we reached a vet. Hardest thing I ever had to do. Damn
your dog!'

'I'm sorry, Fred. I'll bring Bessie back home. I've got to get back
anyways.'

Fred stops crying and whistles. It's a loud, somewhat eerie whistle.
Bessie stops barking and runs up to him. 'I'll be damned,' he says.
He pets her hindquarters. He picks up a stick and throws it. Bessie
brings it right back. 'I'll be damned. That ugly mutt has a brain.'
He laughs.

He continues throwing the stick, petting Bessie when she returns. 'Damn dog, you're quick,' he laughs.

Bill opens the gate quietly and slips into his house.

A few hours later, he looks out his window and sees Fred and
Bessie taking a walk. She's not even on a leash, just walking by his
side as if they've been doing this for years.

The next morning before he heads to school, he's surprised to see Fred using a fancy pooper-scooper. This thing has to be at least four feet long. He's nowhere near the poop. He's a pro at this. Bessie's chasing a squirrel.

At school, Liz doesn't ask him about his first night with the dog. She never will.

Diane Payne teaches creative writing at University of Arkansas-Monticello, where she is also faculty advisor of Foliate Oak Literary Magazine. She is the author of two novels: Burning Tulips and A New Kind of Music. She has been published in hundreds of literary magazines. More info can be found here: http://home.earthlink.net/~dianepayne/

Digs

By Gavin Marshall

I arrived home late one night,
with soft light from the artificial fire
glowing in the living room. Lying
on the sofa was my father and
as I sneaked by he called on me:

Son, ye huvnae paid yur digs this week,
when um a gaunie get thim?
Ye know yur sistur son? Seventeen an payin'
digs, how old are ye now? auld enough yet, aye?
When a wis yur age son a hud a motor,
an' a moustache an' a could pay ma digs.
a know whit yur problem is son, ye need direction,
mare importantly though, ye need tae pay yur digs.
It's good ye've got yur education son, am no denyin' that,
but digs are just a fact o' life an' that's the truth.
Where ye gonnae live if ye cannae pay yur digs?
Son am only daein' this fur yur ain benefit.
Twenty year auld an' still werring a school bag,
ur ye no embarrassed son? A wid be, a hud ma ain drill at sixteen.
Ma faither used tae sit on the couch an' grab ma digs
oaf me son, are ye no glad a dinnae dae that tae ye?

'Cheers Da'.
And I sulked off to my bedroom,
Life chiselled to nothing.
I carried my schoolbag,
and had no money in my pockets.

Gavin Marshall is a Glasgow-based Web Copywriter who discovered a passion for writing during his time at Stirling University. His literary influences include Jack Kerouac, Tom Leonard and Hubert Selby Jnr - although he does not believe that the first thought always equals the best thought. Forthcoming projects include a collection of poetry and artwork with rising Scottish illustrator Gregor Loudon and during 2010 he plans to begin work on a novel set in Glasgow.

No' For the Likes O' Us
By Linda Menzies

It wisnae really lik' Ma tae swear, so Ah kent she wis really upset aboot the bairn. Then she went aff her heid when Ah telt her aboot the other thing. Ah dinnae blame her in a way, it's jist too much for her tae cope wi'. I jist miss her, that's a'.

But see, it's when Ah look at ma bairn, ma wee lassie, Ah cannae stop greetin' sometimes. It's lik' someone's turnt on a tap in ma heid, an' the water a' gushes oot ma e'en.

She's such a wee darlin', wi' yon big broon e'en, an' it jist disnae seem richt, somehow. Ah aye feel worse aboot it a' when Ah've bin up at the hospital.

Ah've aye liked bairns. Ah liked lookin' efter ma wee brither an' sister, takin' them tae the park, an' up in the bus tae the toon near Christmas time tae see the lichts an' yon big tree. We'd gae in the shops but Billy, the wee bugger, wid aye lose interest efter a wee while, an' start muckin' aboot near the posh china, so we'd hae tae gae sharpish afore he hauled doon Edinburgh Crystal ontae the flair an' got us chucked oot.

Ma wee sister Charlene liked tae see a' the toys though, yon big lot o' fluffy teddies an' cuddly big dogs wi' glittery collars. Her e'en went a' big an' bricht an' she used tae gae a' still, jist lookin' an' lookin' at a' they thoosands o' toys. Ah dinnae really ken why I used tae tak' her, for it aye made me that vexed that she couldnae hae any o' they things. 'Tak' me tae the shops', she'd say though, every Christmas, an' Ah aye took them.

Ah aye wanted ma ain hame. Ah used tae dream aboot it, an' imagine whit a proper hame wid be lik'. Some days Ah'd look oot the windae o' oor flat, fourteen flairs up in the sky, an' look at the bleak grey street. There'd be a burnt-oot car, lik' a bluitered man lopsided, lollin' against the kerb, rusty door hangin' aff its hinges. The street wid swirl wi' scraps o' newspaper, an' crisp packets, an' there'd be laddies hangin' roond the Spar. They'd flick their fag ends onto the slimy street, an' spit onto the pavement - disgusting.

Auld folk, wearin' trainers an' scabby coats rich wifies frae the Perth Road gave tae the Oxfam shop, wid stand waitin' for the post office tae open. Ah aye think why should auld folk hae tae come oot in a' weathers tae get their wee bit money, an' hae tae watch a' they shutters bein' takin' doon, lik' it wis a fortress keepin' them oot?

Oor hoose wisnae up tae much, although Ma did try her best. It wis hard tae keep oor claes clean wi' nae washin' machine, an' she didnae hae enough money tae get the food in that she wanted. It used tae mak' me laugh when they telt us at the skil aboot fresh fruit an' veg bein' guid for ye. If ye're livin' on benefits, ye buy chips an' pies that fill up yir belly, niver mind the broccoli.

Anyway, Ah used tae look oot the windae an' think that ma dream hoose wid no' be set in a huge, grim scheme where snotty-nosed bairns skipped skil tae sniff glue an' smoke Embassy Regals they'd nicked frae the paper shop. Ah'll tell ye aboot ma fantasy hoose in a meenute. Ah can picture a' sorts o' details, an' ma ideal hame life widnae feature the polis liftin' the man o' the hoose at regular intervals, lik' whit happened wi' ma Da.

Ma Da wisnae even a success at bein' a villain - he aye got caught, whether he wis floggin' nicked Game Boys or breakin' intae hooses. Ma wid jist shrug her shooders when he wis awa' again, an' then she'd get on wi' it.

But for someone lik' me, frae whit they ca' 'deprived circumstances', Ah hae whit Mrs Pearson ma auld English teacher caud 'a not insubstantial amount of grey matter' an' 'a fertile imagination'. Mrs Pearson wis dead nice, an' used tae lend me her ain books tae read.

'You should aim for university, Lisa', she said.

Ah micht as weel hae aimed for the moon. Ma did gae doon tae the skil yin day when Mrs Pearson wrote tae her, but she came back an' jist said: 'Am sorry ma hen, there's jist nae way ye kin stay on at the skil, even wi' they grants she spoke aboot. Ah need ye tae work wi' yir Da bein' awa'. Yon Mrs Pearson says yir guid at writin' an' Ah ken that masel. But its no' for the likes o' us'

So Ah worked in a shoe shop, an' got books frae the library. Ah fair liked that 'Sunset Song', ye ken yon auld book aboot the country-side up in Aberdeenshire, an' yon Chris Guthrie. It soonded jist great up there, an' Ah used tae dream aboot bein' a farmer's wife, wi' lots o' lovely bairns, an' a' yon fresh, green countryside.

There'd be a cosy log fire, wi' breid bakin' in the oven. an' me sittin' knittin' o' a winter's nicht while me an' ma man watched the telly, wi' the snow an' wind batter' the auld stone fairmhoose. I'd hae loads o' books, of course, an' ma bairns wid a' be brainy an' guid lookin'. Ah'd hae loads o' nice freends in the cottages roond aboot, an' Ah'd gae tae concerts in the village hall, an' watch ma bairns singin' on the stage.

An' there'd be room in ma hoose for Ma an' ma brither an' sister; they could stay an' play oot in the fields or doon by the stream. It wid be dead healthy for them. Ma could sit an' watch the telly, or help me do few wee chores, nothin' too much, but jist a bit tae keep her hand in, like, an' yon worried look wid gae aff her face.

But a' o' that wis cloud cuckoo land, an' aboot as likely as me ga'en tae university.

Ah kent Rab- that's Jessie's Da- wis intae drugs an' a' that stuff when Ah first met him. Ye cannae live doon oor bit withoot gettin' tae ken a' the bad lads - the druggies, boozers, car nickers an' the rest o' the dodgy yins. Ma said: 'Keep awa' frae that yin, Lisa, he's bad news.'

But whit are ye like at 16? He had a braw smile, affae white teeth an' dimples, wid' ye believe? He wis affae cute, an' a great laugh - niver a dull meenute wi' him aroond.

Ah didnae lik' him shootin' up - grass or a few pills is yin thing, but the needle's somethin' else.

'Dinnae worry sae much aboot me', he'd say, an' gie' me a big sloppy kiss, then we'd gae oot for a cairryoot.

Ma wis richt though. He jist didnae want tae ken aboot the bairn. When Ah telt him Ah wis up the stick, he jist bolted. Maybe he kent he wisnae weel by that time anyway, but Ah niver saw him for dust. Niver saw him again, full stop, unless ye coont his funeral. Funny enough, he didnae die the way Ah thoucht he wid - he wis stabbed ootside some pub yin nicht by a so-ca'd mate. It wis aboot drugs money - there's a surprise. There wis aye some bloke efter him.

Ah had the bairn, an' here we are in this cooncil flat in Whitfield - Ma didnae want tae ken aboot the bairn. She telt me: 'Ah've enough tae dae withoot bringin' up yir wee bastard an' a'. Christ knows there's no' enough tae gae roond as it is.'

She doesnae need any mair worries, Ah ken, but maybe Ah wis jist hopin' she wid hae helped me wi' everythin'. It's when Ah've had they nicht sweats an' Ah wake up feelin' really crap, an' scared, Ah wish ma wis here wi' me, lik' when I wis wee an' had a bad dream. She'd cuddle me up wi' her an' stroke ma hair until Ah calmed doon. 'Ye've got such bonnie hair ma lamb,' she'd say, 'it's jist lik' silk.'

The doctor telt me yin day: 'You've been really unlucky, Lisa, there's usually so much more we can do these days. But we think your pregnancy has speeded things up, and the drugs regimes we've tried don't seem to be working.'

Whit wis Ah supposed tae say tae that? Yon doctor didnae look auld enough tae hae tae be tellin' folk a' this bad stuff - he looked knackered an' a'. Yin bit o' ma brain wis thinkin' it must be crap for him an' a'. He must feel bad seein' a young lassie lik' me here. The only thing that is lucky is that the bairn is ok- but it fair twists ma guts tae look at her an' ken there's only ga'en tae be a few mair months thegither.

Last week, we got the bus an' went doon tae Broughty Ferry. Ah pit her in yon buggy the social worker got me, an' Ah walked doon tae the beach, pointin' oot a' the shops an' cars an' things tae her. She tried tae grab a wee broon dug sittin' ootside a fruit shop, an' she swivelled richt roond watchin' it, as I pushed her doon the street, Then she spotted a massive bunch o' balloons tied up ootside a wee newsagents, an' made as if tae get them an' a.'

Ah boucht her a pink an' silver yin wi' 'it's a girl' on it. It wis really for folk takin' tae the hospital for a new baby, but Ah thoucht, whit the hell, we niver got balloons or flooers, or even a card, come tae think o' it, when she wis born. She can hae it noo.

We went richt doon ontae the beach. it wis freezin' cauld, wi' the wind blawin' intae oor faces. They seagulls made a hell o' a racket, but the bairn pit up her wee hands, tryin' tae grab them an' a'. Her wee mittens were half aff, an' Ah cuddled her up close an' ticht as Ah pit them back on again.

'Silly Jessie, kept yir hands cosy!' Ah telt her, laughin' an' kissin' her wee cauld cheeks.

She started laughin' an' a', an' pulled ma hair. Then she said 'Mum mum,' her first words.

Ah thoucht ma heirt wis ga'en tae brak' richt there an' then on yon beach, wi' the frothy waves crashin' a few yards awa'. See, suddenly Ah kent whit it wid hae bin lik' for us. Ah'd hae loved her always. A wid hae made a life for us somehow, an' Ah wid hae made sure she had a' they chances Ah didnae get. She wid hae made me strong, made me better too.

Richt then, Ah hated Rab. It bubbled up in me lik' a poison. He wis tae blame for a' o' this. Then Ah looked at Jessie an' saw her smilin' at me wi' his broon e'en. 'The puir bugger's deid, an' there's an end tae it', Ah telt Jessie, an' she wriggled in ma airms.

She's gettin' adopted soon- best thing, the social worker says, so she can get used tae her new mum an' Da while she's still wee.

When she goes tae her new hame, Ah ken whit Ah'm ga'en tae dae. It'll soond daft tae ye, Ah ken, but Ah'm ga'en tae clear oot o' Dundee, an' ga'en up north an' see if Ah can find the red earth an sweepin' skies in 'Sunset Song'. Ah'll find a job until ma health finally braks doon, then Ah'm ga'en tae find a wee secret place, an auld ruined bothy an' Ah'm ga'en tae tak' a' they pills Rab left ahind when he scarpered, an' Ah'm jist ga'en tae lie there lookin' at they clouds until the end.

No, ye mustnae greet lik' that. Ah shouldnae hae telt ye a' this, maybe. See, A'll no see it, but whit maks me ok aboot it a' is that ma Jessie's ga'en tae get they chances.

An' maybe yin day when she's grown up, an' on a beach sometimes, an' hears a' they bloody gulls, an' sees a bairn wi' a balloon, she'll catch that wee, distant memory o' her Ma that loved her.

Linda Menzies worked in journalism for many years and is currently working as a public relations officer. She has had a number of poems and short stories published over the years and draws inspiration from the countryside near her Angus home, and 'people watching.'

CV Building
By Rachel Marsh

During her Master's Degree, Janet threw herself into various extra-curricular activities; one particular activity was called a Forum. She was awarded her taught postgraduate degree from an English University; however, that particular University is not the only institution to hold such gatherings, nor are they the only University to believe that by linking these events to ancient Greece through its name, it would conjure an atmosphere in which underlings (students) sat at the feet of intellectual elite (lecturers) hoping to gratefully taste, even if only briefly, the radiance of their masters. Universities across the United Kingdom list Forums on their schedules hoping to fulfil some sort of open-discussion remit fostered by bored student government bodies.

The title Forum rarely lives up to the name's hype. As Janet was matriculated in the School of English, English literature debates were her forte. At these Literature Forums, postgraduates give presentations on their research (undergraduates only attended when attempting to appear studious to their PG tutors), and -- as

English postgraduates are fond of judging others based on word
choice, syntax and grammar -- power-points, outlines, pictures,
diagrams or any other tool that may help to make the presentation
interesting were banned. Instead, the students were encouraged
to stand at a podium and read from an essay or chapter for forty
minutes. It was the job of those in the audience -- other postgraduates,
lecturers and staff -- to not fall asleep, and, after the paper was
finished, to question word choice, syntax and grammar. Then once
that round of 'questioning' had been completed, various members of
the audience would stand, compare the research presented to their
own work and make general comments about their own findings,
which usually had nothing to do with the paper presented at the
Forum.

Rarely did the 'masters' attend, and only did so when a new Head
of Department sent an email suggesting Forum attendance by staff
would be linked to grant funding. The faculty's attendance only
lasted until they got their RAE results, at which point everyone
sighed briefly and ignored all students – both undergraduate and
postgraduate.

While completing her Master's degree, Janet had become
extremely familiar with the Forum experience, and in three years
as a PhD student in Scotland she did not attend one Postgraduate
Forum or event. Not even the beginning of term wine receptions.
But with a submission deadline in the not so distance future, she
felt like she needed some form of critical feedback; something she
was not getting from her supervisor; so she decided to turn to her
peers and hope for the best. Not comfortable with being new at the
Forum, she did not want to immediately volunteer to give a paper.
So she planned on appearing at a few sessions, before suggesting
that she present at a later date. She hoped that eventually presenting
a thesis chapter would not only act as a free copyediting service,
but some of the comments might help her decide whom to avoid as
an external examiner.

The Forum was held in a room with windows on three sides, one
wall of windows looking out over a tree-lined park. The organiser
-- a PhD student studying 'The Literatures of the Telemarketing
Industry in Mumbai as a Post-Revolutionary link to Joseph Smith

and the early Mormons' -- had shut all the windows and turned up
the heating, in order to dull all senses and limber the body, creating
an atmosphere most similar to a Bikram yoga studio on a hot day
in the desert. He had also pulled all the blinds, in order to keep out
any extra-sensory distractions, such as a beautiful blue sky on a
warm spring day.

The first speaker began with a quotation from Dostoevsky's letter to
Nikolay Stachov, which he would never admit to finding on Wikipedia:

*What most people regard as fantastic and lacking in universality,
I hold to be the inmost essence of truth. Arid observation of everyday
trivialities I have long since ceased to regard as realism – it is quite
the reverse. In any newspaper one takes up, one comes across reports
of wholly authentic facts, which nevertheless strike one as extraordinary.
Our writers regard them as fantastic, and take no account of them;
and yet they are the truth, for they are facts. But who troubles to
observe, record, describe them? They happen everyday and every
moment, therefore they are not 'exceptional'.*

The student then stated, 'I will take the audacious attitude that
Dostoevsky is a hack, and the true form of reality, the beauty in it,
lies not in the exceptional but in the banality of life.' At this point a
small girl, with a pointed nose that failed to do its only two jobs –
breath without wheezing and hold up a pair of glasses – suggested
that the speaker should have not used the word 'banality' but
instead should have used 'mundaneness'. A twenty minute argument then ensued regarding word choice, until the girl with the
pointed nose left the room declaring to never return. The speaker
then resumed his talk by proceeding to read a short story of his
own creation. The only thing that happened in this story was that a
character used the toilet, in graphic detail.

After the initial speaker, four more students gave presentations.
Two read poems, one person read a short story, and a forth discussed
the act of writing creatively. Each piece was to be original, but the
students were obviously influenced by their academic research. One
poem was in Shakespearean sonnet form but written in a language
originated by Tolkien, another was titled 'A Love Poem to Alfred P.

Jufrock', and the short story called 'The Lottery' was an attempt to take irony from the original story -- at the end the woman wins the lottery and lives happily ever after having put her money in a high-yield long-term investment portfolio. Everything was 'original' but with obvious homage.

Janet pulled the Forum schedule from her bag, perhaps she had mistakenly decided to attend on the day that the 'creative writing' students were slotted to share their work. Janet was in the English department, but was of the 'literary' branch and had very little to do with the creative writers who wandered about the halls of the department. They made her uncomfortable, coming to the University to write poems and make things up. She often felt resentment towards these students, and felt that all they had to do to get a degree was rhyme a few words or come up with a little story, while she spent hours trying to understand the deep meanings of the world's greatest minds. The creative writers often made statements like, 'Without us, you'd have nothing nor anyone to research.' Janet's answer to this was 'So, you think you're Virginia Woolf?' These creative writers were not simply a Rorschach blot on prestigious ancient and redbrick institutions, but all Universities – even the lesser institutions like those across the Tay -- were now accepting these tradesmen-style academics called creative writers, and while those studying physics didn't have to share an office with a plumber or an electrician, the great literary minds of Britain were forced to sit next to a potential Rowling. Many felt the shame to be unbearable.

Janet looked at the schedule to see when the 'academics' spoke at the Forum and when the 'creatives' spoke, but the paper stated that this day was an 'academic' slot. She raised her hand and said, 'I'm a bit confused. I thought this Forum was for academic papers.'

The group responded in a manner similar to a Greek Chorus:

'It is for the critic to be the artist.'

'How can we judge lest we be judged?'

'It is the aspect of art that is the critical judgement.'

'Are not creative-writing students, but creative writing-students,' said one man making air quotes with his fingers at the appropriate stresses.

There was a bit of rumbling and murmuring amongst the

statements.

'Does everyone here write creatively?' Janet asked.

There was more rumbling of voices and a nodding of heads to suggest the question was ridiculous. Janet followed-up with the question, 'Doesn't this get in the way of your academic work?'

A large puffy man, with a great head of curly hair stood up, 'Everyone's writing these days. No one goes into academia without having a book of poetry or a novel on the go. It's our form of expression outside our academic pursuits.'

'Do you ever mix the two?' Janet asked.

Everyone laughed in a hardy but polite way, except for the four people in the back with eyes closed and spittle dripping down their cheek -- the sauna-like conditions sent them into a transcendental state. Not noticing the slumbering to the rear of the room, the curly-headed man said to Janet, 'Oh of course not. Creativity does not have its place in research, and literary criticism has no place in the creation of art. But we all do both: separate but equal. It's the modern academic's lot to multi-task.'

'So do the creative writing students now do academic research?' Janet followed.

The room filled with roaring laughter, and it was a few minutes before it fell to a soft snicker, allowing the curly-headed man to say, 'Heavens no. They don't have the wit or intelligence for it.'

A girl, slouching back in her chair, black hair across her eyes, stated, 'I've learned from my supervisor's mistakes. He's been fighting the creatives for decades. I think these "creative writers" are a lazy breed and a part of the capitalistic force that has desecrated contemporary society, but by being a creative myself I can take their power and give it back to those who deserve it – the research-ers.'

Then the man with the helmet of curled hair spoke again, 'Plus it's good for the C.V.'

'Oh yes,' the angry woman in black stated. 'It's easier to get a little story published than an academic article. And, well, you know, publish or perish. And if that means writing a measly little haiku here or there, then so be it.'

Janet went home that evening thinking of her future. It had

already been drilled into her head that if she wanted to succeed in academia she'd have to publish monographs and journal articles, but no one told her that she had to write creatively as well. It was something she had never done and had never found a desire to do. She enjoyed exposing, discovering, and interpreting facts. Yes, she enjoyed literature and fiction, but she was far more comfortable reporting than creating. She didn't see the appeal in making things up. However, if she was to get ahead, to find a career in a University setting, she would need to add this one trait to her Curriculum Vitae. That evening Janet sat down to write a short story.

With a blank computer screen she thought, 'Write what you know.' Initially she decided to write about being a former economic journalist in a tiny Scottish town filled with Americans, but after two pages she realised that she was writing a feature story, recalling quotes from people she'd heard on the high street and figures she'd seen in the newspaper.

She'd try again. 'This time, something wild,' she thought. 'A spaceship.' In a page she described Dr Who's tree-like tardis. Janet was feeling imbecilic for her inability to imagine the non-existent.

She thought about what was popular at the moment — shock. Contemporary literature, especially that of Scotland, seemed to have the aim of shocking, which was terribly hard when the average dour Scottish reader revelled in how hard their own life was. But she turned her hand to it anyway and wrote a page about a self-harming, anorexic streetwalker in the grimiest area of Glasgow and her heroine addicted husband who was also a child abusing pimp. There was a murder, and by the end of the page she was about to introduce a hard-boiled Detective with an ex-wife and a drink problem. Reading the page back to herself, she realised the story had become Ian Rankin writing for iTV. She deleted the whole thing and began with another topic.

She pulled from the shelf a collection of short stories written by women and flipped through it. What did they write about, and how did they do it? Janet found scenes of everyday life, written in excruciating detail--as if it was happening in slow motion. Perhaps the skinny fellow at the Forum was correct. That the Russian writer was wrong and that reality and creativity collided in the mundane details of the every day.

Janet tipped her hand at realism:

The desk-drawer slid open a crack. Oak with a light stain, the wood was beginning to fade as the sun's light streamed through the window, hitting the same patch of the desk for the last six years. Inside the desk, laying on top of a manila folder -- whose contents remained unimportant, as the owner of the drawer hadn't looked at that folder since its placement there three years prior -- was a ham sandwich wrapped in brown paper.

Hazel reached into the drawer, her large hand scraping the sides of the drawer; she felt for the brown paper, it was making a rustling noise as she wrapped her thick fingers around the bulk and pulled it out and into the open air.

She placed the package on a clear spot on her desk; she could smell the mustard through the bag, and Hazel closed her eyes in anticipation. Her mouth was beginning to water like one of Pavlov's' dogs, but she refused to rush her lunch break as it was the only piece of solitude stolen in her otherwise manic life.

The woman carefully unwrapped the paper from the sandwich starting with the left fold, then the right. Hazel gazed down upon the lunch item, and the whiteness of the bread reminded her of the elderflowers in her grandmother's hedgerows, and the pink of the ham sneaking out from beneath the bread was the colour of her lover's hairless chin. Hazel pushed her hand down upon the sandwich, which left prints unique to herself...

'God. This shit is boring,' Janet thought. 'Why can't I just say, "In an old desk drawer she found a ham sandwich and ate it".' Anyhow, she was getting hungry; it was time for dinner, and she fancied a ham sandwich. Janet closed the document and saved it as 'Hazel Eats a Sandwich.' As she went to fix her dinner, she wondered what she would ever do with that silly document, and had no idea why she saved it. If what she had written belonged to another author, to someone other than herself, she'd find the relevance of metaphor against alliteration; she'd use Freudian, Jungian and Gynocritical theories to analyse a myriad of representations and symbols. But she found writing fiction tedious; she was much happier as a journalist, an academic and a reader of fiction. She had no desire to create, despite what sort of a blank it left on the C.V.

Rachel believes that she has found the secret to getting her short stories published – edit the anthology. Rachel, a long-time postgraduate student, is submitting her thesis on Eric Linklater in the fall and is afraid of what might happen to her writing career once she's left the University of Dundee. 'C.V. Building' is an extract from her novel Gynocriticism (which is a 'true life story' about a literal man-eating monster on a menstrual rampage in a small Scottish town), and would like to offer her editorial services to any major publishing house in exchange for a three-book publishing deal and a Hollywood film offer.

Enter Magnus
By Catherine Oxford

E arlier that same afternoon, in a leafy neighbourhood not far from Gladstone Terrace, in the spacious conservatory of Ashdene, a detached Victorian manor which stood on its own extensive and bird-filled gardens, Magnus Bairson, the famous writer of non-fiction novels in the genre of In Cold Blood, was watching a football match on television.

The television was, like the rest of the décor, tastefully understated: not one of those uncouth plasma creations with a thousand satellite channels, but a modest flat screen with a basic cable service, evidence that Magnus Bairson was neither a television fan nor, by any stretch of the term, a football fan. Why a famous writer – beer and chips in hand, lying upon an over-stuffed teak sofa in nothing but his boxers and a worn-out seersucker dressing gown – engaged in an activity that held no interest for him whatsoever is, for now at least, a matter of some curiosity, if not yet a matter of crucial importance.

However, it is not quite true to say that Magnus Bairson, forty-eight and firmly stuck in a toxic marriage to Ruthie and with two grown yet unemployed children (Pippa and Geoff, who still sponged off him as occasion demanded), was a famous writer. More accurately, he had been a famous writer, but on this particular afternoon, as he lounged on the sofa amid birdsong and summer sunshine, he was less famous for being a writer as for having been a famous writer. After a string of bestsellers through his thirties, and after a decade of critical acclaim which saw him feted on Oprah, revered at all the major book festivals from Edinburgh to Perth — Perth, Australia, of course — and hailed in all the seriously grown-up papers as "the most compelling new voice of his generation", his muse had for some reason deserted him. Nowadays, to the exasperation of his agent and his publisher, he was piffling away whole years in some second-rate university, teaching Eng Lit. What a waste of a talent, all agreed, including Magnus Bairson himself, who despite his stoic demeanour, was growing angrier with and more despairing of himself by the moment. His general lassitude, his state of undress, his exasperation with his children and his wife — speaking of whom, not to mention his sex life—, his fixed and expressionless countenance in which the only movement was his mouth, opening to receive yet another fistful of salt-and-vinegar chips, were all clues to his true condition: Magnus Bairson was teetering on the precipice of depression and staring down into the black abyss of a mid-life crisis. From such positions, people are often liable to do things that look very strange or silly to others but that make perfect sense to them.

For now, he seemed content to teeter. Downing the dregs of the beer he balled up the empty chip bag with a vicious crackle and pulled out his laptop. Perhaps he had been struck by a ray of inspiration? Perhaps he was about to tap out the perfectly-formed first sentence of his next novel, which had just bubbled up from the sludge of his unconscious?

No such luck. Often, Magnus idly surfed through his favourite porn sites: LoveBites. Pretty Dumb Things. At least his preferences in porn nodded in the direction of literary sophistication: the writing was wickedly smart, the debauchery rife with overtones of John Cleland, undertones of Montmartre in the Twenties, and asides to

Shakespeare. He never felt any guilt in throbbing to Mick's slick photo-essays of Dee in bondage or to Chelsea Girl's rococo meditations on her deep-throating techniques. After all, the allusions to Ovid in Mick's commentaries were obvious, and Chelsea was working on a PhD in Restoration rhetoric from Columbia, no less. It was porn for intellectuals, porn that made you feel good about yourself, not only as a man but as a thinker. Porn that uplifted you in more ways than one. Besides, Magnus could always explain his interest as professional: it was a well-known fact that his study housed a small yet impressive collection of museum-quality Victorian pornography. After one excited survey, the university librarian had pleaded with him for a bequest, the 'Bairson Bequest – we can dedicate a whole section, hell, maybe even a room!'

And here is a little secret that Magnus would not want shared with anyone: he had never in his life had anything but the most humdrum sex with Ruthie, and the one thing he wanted more than anything, almost more than to smash through this cursed block and write another book, was to have the wildest, most uninhibited sex imaginable with a woman who would beg him to master her.

Just once, he wanted to taste something so filthy, so outrageously delicious that it would thrill him from the roots of his hair to the tips of his toes. Just once, he wanted to chow down on super hot-fudge-sundae sex, triple chocolate decadence sex with toothsome mouthfuls of nutty, moist brownies. Kept on a lifetime diet of bald vanilla delivered once a month in prim scoops (if he was lucky), Magnus craved the biggest, gooiest, and slurpiest of all-day quadruple pineapple-banana split sex oozing with warm honey and studded with plump cherries sliding down mountains of whipped cream into oceans of velvety butterscotch, pineapple, and black raspberry syrup sex – oh glory of knicker-fucking-bocker glories sex! To submerge yourself in that, to come up for air with your face and limbs streaming with it, to gasp and laugh and dive headfirst into it again, over and over, until it took away all your hunger and thirst! Was it so much to ask?

The pleasant hot-air balloon ride of his daydream ended with a thump when Ruthie suddenly poked her perfectly-coiffed head around the door. Lavender-scented and lavender-suited, she was

slightly breathless and still all a-bustle from her meeting of the
Friends of the Botanic Garden, of which she was chairperson. She
frowned at him – her default setting, although she never came away
from these meetings in a very good mood.

It always amused him, how rife with controversy and discord
were these gatherings of plant fanciers. Genteel and decorous ladies
whose all-butter fruitbread melted in your mouth, and who single-
handedly maintained the stone fabric of their churches with their
spring fetes and harvest festivals could apparently take fits at the
merest mention of an incorrectly pruned forsythia. Experience
had taught him that Ruthie herself was quite capable of coming to
blows about the proper method of fertilising semi-succulent alpines.

And here she was, flushed, and no doubt still pumped from some
confrontation about clematis – always a touchy botanical topic, he
knew –, pursing her lips at his state of undress and clucking like
an old hen. 'For God's sake, Magnus. I told you to pick up my dry-
cleaning this afternoon. Never mind, I'll do it myself.'

She was gone before he could offer an olive branch. He sighed
and said to the air, 'Sorry, dear. I'll start the supper.' If there was
one thing Magnus Bairson loved almost as much as porn, it was
cooking. Spending hours getting up to all sorts in the kitchen was
almost as fun, he imagined, as doing the same in the bedroom. Not
that he had any experience of that. But even if the allusion escaped
Ruthie, he prided himself on being a dab hand with a mortar and
pestle, and at least his cooking never made her list of complaints.

Clicking the wholly succulent Chelsea shut with a sigh, he belted
his gown over the wilting evidence of his daydreams of decadence
and heaved himself upright, ruefully reflecting that even though he
did all the cooking, Ruthie set the menu in this house, and super
sinful sundae sex would not be on it any time soon.

*Catherine Oxford moved to Dundee from Canada to escape winter. No, seriously.
Skittish by nature, she publishes short fiction under various pseudonyms in
order to avoid being pinned down. Enter Magnus is an excerpt from her current
novel-in-progress.*

The Prologue (To Everything that Came Before)

By Hope Jennings

Ten years after the last time he saw either of his brothers, Jamie Brennan sat alone in a first-class compartment on the journey from Paris to Lausanne. He contemplated the countryside revealed to him like a film played out in reverse motion across the transparent, though slightly smudged, screen of glass. At one point he was startled by the reflection of his face imprinted onto the rolling scenery passing by, the optical illusion presenting a seeming paradox, as if he were simultaneously present in two different spatial and temporal realms. He recalled, with some irritation, that his father had once observed this very same uncanny, involuntary doubling. Though Jamie could not isolate the exact novel in which that mirrored scene of his thoughts originated, no doubt his father would have expressed it far more eloquently than himself.

As a consolation, Jamie retrieved a fading black and white photograph from his left breast pocket, studying it for perhaps the hundredth time since he'd first seen it. The waif offered him a sullen scowl of distrust. A tumble of black curls framed her pale, heart-shaped face, slightly tilted to one side in a pose of defiance, her wide, black eyes coldly, contemptuously challenging whoever stood behind the camera. When Jamie first met the woman who'd refused to remain frozen in that single, awkward moment of her childhood, he'd immediately recognized her. One look into her eyes and he'd known she was the spectral revenant of that little girl notoriously evoked by his father in nearly all of his books published over the past twenty years.

The photograph had confirmed Jamie's long-held suspicions: his father's claim on fictional integrity was a fraud. Although Vasili habitually insisted, in countless interviews, letters, and dinner-hour debates, that he'd never plundered his autobiography for the purposes of writing fiction, this statement had always carried the stench of a disingenuous protestation. Jamie knew for a fact, having made a detailed comparative study between the intersecting imaginative processes of schizophrenics and novelists, one's reality had a habit of creeping into one's fantasies; or, one's fantasies infected the reality. His father was not exempt from this phenomenon, though he managed to display greater skill than most novelists in concealing the details of his life within the details of stories about lives he refused to claim as his own. Now, in spite of his father's denials, Jamie had proof of his theorem. The great master of artifice, Vasili Novikov, was guilty of stealing from his own life, and the lives of others, and had failed to disguise certain events and personages as wholly fictionalized creations.

This discovery, however, had taken Jamie some time to digest. After receiving the photograph from its former subject, who'd shown up unexpectedly on his doorstep after more than three years of searching for his missing brother, Jamie pulled down each of his father's novels from the shelves and methodically searched all the relevant passages, glancing occasionally, anxiously at the woman who slept on his sofa for the better part of two days. When she finally woke, he summoned the nerve to ask if she was that same girl his father had repeatedly reincarnated. She'd laughed, nodding, then remarked: 'It was always just variations on a theme, and he actually never knew me as a child.' No, of course, he couldn't have, Jamie demurred, calculating the years, but the photograph still lay

between them as evidence. So she'd had no choice but to tell him
her version of the story.

Jamie put away the photograph, not sure if he would have the
courage to show it to his father. Besides, if what she'd said was
true, and she had no reason to lie, then Vasili had already seen the
image at least twice before; there was no point in destroying him
with this souvenir of all that he'd lost. He was the only son his father
had left, and the burden of this role was something Jamie felt he
could no longer manage. He too wanted to vanish and become only
a character in one of his father's books, precisely because this was
the only means Vasili had of becoming reconciled with the past.

Jamie willed himself into a doze, refusing to dream, declining
to wake until the train pulled into the station. There would not
be anyone waiting for him at the platform. No one was expecting
him. He hired a taxi to drive him the fifteen miles to his parent's
small villa tucked away in the sloping hills surrounding Lausanne,
the last place they'd decided to call home. He had not brought any
luggage, as he was planning on immediately returning to Paris,
and so had nothing to set down by the front door to announce his
arrival. A meaningless gesture, since his mother now depended on
a hearing device, which she rarely deigned to attach to her ear. As
for his father, he would be sitting in the garden, beneath the broad
shade of the tulip poplar, and counting all the real and imagined
butterflies, wafting temptingly above his head, which he was no
longer agile enough to pursue with his madly wavering net.

Jamie padded up softly behind his mother, who sat at the kitchen
table sorting through the never-ending pile of mail, and gave her
bony shoulder a gentle squeeze. She absently murmured hello,
unsurprised to find him there, and continued with her menial task
of correspondence with the outside world, the sort of thing his father
had always left up to her. He sat and waited until she decided to
raise her elegant, silvery head, slip her spectacles from her beaky,
dignified, nose, and directly acknowledge his presence.

'You should have told us you were coming,' she reprimanded
Jamie.

'It's only for the afternoon.'

'Your father will be disappointed,' she left no doubt that she equally referred to herself.

'How is he?' Jamie asked.

'He is as well as he has ever been,' she offered, which, considering Vasili's mercurial moods, implicated anything ranging from manic elation to suicidal ennui.

'Now, why don't you go say hello? He'll be thrilled to see you, and I'm sure you have important matters to discuss.'

'Actually there's something I need to tell both of you,' Jamie was breaking the rules; she'd always preferred to have whatever news her sons might have brought with them to be repeated to her later, privately, by her husband.

'Oh?' she lifted one thinly drawn brow into an acute arch, an incomplete question mark, as if she simply had to wait and sooner or later the information would be revealed to her without expending the energy of acquiring it.

'I'm going to be married,' Jamie blurted, knowing it was the only way.

'You are too old for marriage,' she laughed indulgently. 'Really, Jamie, you are nearly forty-years-old. Can you imagine what our lives might have been like if I'd married your father when he was that age? It would have been quite impossible!'

Yes, Jamie thought, impossible that any of her sons might have been born; for once, he refused to allow his mother to distill the unknown complexities of his life into a convenient analogy that mirrored his father's own stubborn peculiarities.

'I appreciate your concern, mama, but it is decided,' he informed her, dismissively, cruelly. 'I only wanted to tell you in person.'

'Oh dear, how considerate of you.' She feared the redundancy of her old age; her thoughts relegated to the nattering complaints of an inconsequential crone, even if she'd rarely offered her opinions before, at least when it mattered most to do so. 'You always were a conscientious little boy. Are you at least going to tell me the name of this woman?'

Jamie inwardly cringed. He had no choice. 'Mina Byrne.'

Deirdre did not erupt into a tempest of fury; she simply slipped on her familiar, glacial mask, though Jamie detected the faint trace of appalled outrage in her eyes. Mina Byrne would not leave his

mother alone. Miss Byrne had always been intent on stealing for
herself every last possession of Mrs. Novikov. Jamie waited for the
words she would use to disown him, but the words that did come
were the ones his mother always wielded, translating everything of
significance back to her husband.

'You're aware of what this will do to your father,' she stated.

'It won't destroy him,' Jamie weakly insisted. 'Nothing that
happens, no matter how awful, is capable of destroying him.'

'So you'd like to make a go of it yourself. Of course, your brothers
had to, so why not you as well? I never expected it of you, Jamie.
My God, you know nothing of this woman, or you would not be
marrying her!'

'I know everything, mama,' he coolly silenced her, aware she
would not want him to name what that word, everything, contained,
because then she would have to reveal her own complicity in
covering up the facts. 'Besides, papa writes it all down in his
books. He needs some way of communicating the truth to the rest of
us.'

'You never wanted to be a part of this family.'

'Did you?' Jamie lobbed his winning point, the victory far from
satisfying.

'Go talk to your father,' she dismissed him, resettling her spectacles
on the perch of her nose. 'And when you're finished, you may leave
by the garden gate. I'll call you a taxi.'

Jamie rose, stooping helplessly to kiss the silvery crown of her
head. She refused to budge, paralyzed by the unwanted ghosts her
son had brought in with him. Jamie hoped this would not be the
last time he saw her. His father, also, did not acknowledge him
until he'd finished reading the last paragraph on the page in the
book he held in his lap. Jamie sat beside him and observed his
gnarled, spidery blue-veined hands, their joints protruding in a
deformed, arthritic contortion, like the hands of an ogre in a fairy
tale, though Jamie could only see their frailty, or at least their
imagined frailty. Vasili eventually glanced up at his son, scowled,
replaced the bookmark in the slim volume, slammed shut its spine
with considerable force, and then lifted the book in the air, shaking
it gleefully beneath Jamie's nose.

'It just arrived by post, first printing, hot and steaming! This one
will throw them all off the scent. Once again, I've slipped a wrench
in their clumsily cogitating brains!' He laughed inanely, to which
Jamie could only reply, 'That good?'

'Oh no, my boy, it is far from good!' Vasili exhorted. 'It is the most
ingenious disappearing act man has ever devised for himself. The
great Houdini would grovel in envy and shame! A fatal sucker-punch
if there ever was one! Have you read it?'

'Yes, papa, of course I have.' Other than his mother, Jamie was
expected to remain his father's most loyal reader. Jamie had, in
fact, not read it. When he'd received the galleys, he'd immediately
handed them over to Mina, allowing her to translate for him Vasili's
convoluted sense of humor, which Jamie no longer had the stamina
or desire to appreciate on his own. It seemed that in this latest of
the great Novikov's books, Novikov had cleverly concealed himself
behind the mask of Novikov, and this achieved, just as Mina herself
had remarked, a sinuously spiraling, self-referring, if not self-
parodying, ever-receding hall of mirrors. Jamie, however, had not
come here to discuss the enigma of his father's slippery intellect.

'Papa, there's something I must tell you...'

'What, you weren't happy with the book? You think it was too
daring, too arrogant of me. I know you always secretly harbor that
opinion about my novels, but –'

'No, papa,' Jamie cut him off, as it was the only way of deflect-
ing Vasili's attention onto himself. "I'm getting married, to Mina
Byrne.'

Once those words were uttered, Jamie saw his father shrivel
and slump into a very old, tired, and yes, frail man. Somehow, and
without explanation, as he knew at this point it would be entirely
unnecessary, Jamie discovered the courage to return to him the
photograph of a young girl who'd come crashing into all their lives.
His father silently accepted the unexpected gift, smiling in incon-
solable recognition. For what seemed like lifetimes, they listened to
the insistent clicking of the early evening cicadas, and the faintly
imperceptible fluttering of a butterfly's translucently filmy iridescent
wings.

'Why her?' Vasili finally asked, presenting a question requiring multiple answers.

'How could it be anyone other than her?' Jamie was sure that this was the sufficient, the correct, answer.

Then he told his father the other piece of information he needed to know; the only thing that could truly matter, because in the end, Mina herself was negligible. Upon hearing these words, the trajectory of Vasili Vasilievich Novikov's life finally reached the precise point where every pattern wove itself into a fabric of the most sublime, the most perceptibly cruel, yet the only possible recovery of all that had been lost. He visibly began to shake with the comprehension of what could never have been, but miraculously, was exactly as it should be.

'I never knew,' his father mumbled, and then turned away from his son, concealing his face with those large, bulbous, twisted hands.

There was nothing left for Jamie to do but rise, turn, and walk away, because the one thing he could not bear to see would be the image of his father weeping. He left the garden gate unlatched, knowing his mother observed his departure from behind the safety of her kitchen window, and that after Jamie vanished, swallowed up by a future she refused to consider, she would step out into the garden and firmly shut close and bar the gate. And all the while his father would be wandering through his pain and his delight at the nascent thought of his new world, his new fabrication of the truth. It would be a brilliant and ambiguously candid configuration of intricate reflections that doubled and perhaps even tripled the smashed, splintered and scattered fragments of his heart. This, Jamie knew, would be the last of his father's fictions.

Hope Jennings is Assistant Professor of English at Wright State University-Lake Campus, where she teaches British Literature and Women's Studies. She received a B.A. from Hunter College, C.U.N.Y and a Ph.D. from the University of St. Andrews. She is currently writing a metafictional biography of the Modernist poet, Mina Loy.

The Telegraph Pole and the Tree (move up)

By Heather McKenzie

Consider the telegraph pole and the tree,
and then decide which you'd rather be.
Alive with the swoosh of the wind through your leaves?
Or dead, but ensuring the world receives
the vital buzz of communication,
connecting us all, nation to nation?
Side by side by the road they stand,
co-existing to serve the land.

Heather McKenzie is originally from Callander, Perthshire. She now lives in Dundee and commutes to work in Fife, finding inspiration for writing in the surroundings on the journey as well as in the social and political landscapes of our time.

Truth, Fiction and the Journalist: An Interview with David Robinson

By J. A. Cosgrove

E ditors beware – The Scotsman's books editor David Robinson is an advocate of slow journalism and thinks there should be a good deal more in British publications.

Don't fret, his version of 'slow' doesn't mean breaking to have a cuppa once you've done an all-important interview, reclining in a chair, feet up, while the news desk suffers a meltdown as a result of your nonchalance. Slow journalism is a form that reporters and feature writers are these days seldom able to explore – and it's probably a fair assumption that those who are afforded the time and resources to get their teeth into a subject are the envy of their peers. Some journalists have spent years of their lives following a story until they became it; lived it, breathed it, were immersed in it – and only then were they capable of constructing a truthful and balanced account of their experiences.

Bradford-born David has been books editor at The Scotsman since 2000 and a journalist for over thirty years. Since joining the North-West Evening Mail in Barrow-in-Furness as a University graduate, he has met and worked with a number of people who write for both the press and publishing markets.

Although he says he would never follow other journalists down fiction route, David did release a collection of his interviews in 2008 called In Cold Ink. The title pays homage to Truman Capote's In Cold Blood, which famously gave birth to the 'non-fiction novel' genre — investigative journalism with a literary voice. So interested was David in Capote's 1966 masterpiece, which tells the story of the 1959 murder of Kansas farming family, the Clutters, Robinson travelled to the USA in 2007 to retrace the writer's steps.

'I've always been fascinated by Capote and In Cold Blood, and I just wanted to know everything about it,' David explains. 'I felt most alive at the moment I was driving west across the Kansas plains towards the story.'

Capote left school aged seventeen and got a job with The New Yorker magazine. After publishing a collection of short stories and novella Breakfast at Tiffany's, he embarked upon a six-year project that would result in In Cold Blood – an immediate bestseller. He delved into the life of small town Holcomb and even befriended the two murderers, who were placed on death row and eventually executed. Capote's integrity and his ability to use people for his own ends have long been questioned. The film Capote (2005) looked into the morality of the writer's information-gathering and how he succeeded in persuading perfect strangers to share the most intimate details of their lives.

Robinson agrees Capote wasn't a model journalist – in 1957, he 'tricked' film star Marlon Brando into an interview by having dinner with him and encouraging him to talk candidly.

'That's an example of him bending the rules – and twisting them out of shape completely,' David says. 'Capote was an incredible egotist – but there was no mention of him in In Cold Blood at all. I think the book is an example of outstanding journalism. It is approached from every angle and each sentence is copper-bottomed.'

Despite famously writing from memory (albeit with the help of researcher, To Kill a Mockingbird author Harper Lee, who accompanied him to interviews) Capote was never caught out for inaccuracy.

'He did have a phenomenal memory and he used it well,' David
explains. 'Tape recorders would have been enormous back then.
He took no notes when interviewing, but Harper Lee and he would
discuss it afterwards. If he was unsure about something, he would
go back. He was obsessive about accuracy. The fact checker at The
New York Times never caught Capote out and journalists came
down to Kansas and tried to catch him out – but none ever did.'

David says Capote was convinced that a straightforward journalist
would not have been able to produce a story as well crafted as In
Cold Blood. 'I think it's harder to write In Cold Blood than to write
a novel about the murder of four people,' he explains. 'What makes
it a brilliant work is that it really does take you there, and you
know you can rely on it. The problem with us journalists is that,
in our daily working lives, we don't go that deep. But when you do,
it just opens up and you realise the difficulty of doing what Capote
was doing.'

So what can journalists learn from authors – and vice versa?
Is one profession nobler than the other? Certainly, the luxury of
spending six years researching a story isn't afforded to many
reporters these days.

'I wasn't a very good daily journalist. I'm not particularly great
at deadlines and I'm a relatively slow writer,' David explains. 'I
hated the idea that every day you had to be an expert on whatever
you were writing about. Ever since I've been at The Scotsman I
have always been on the features.'

David agrees there are limitations to generic style of news reporting, but there is much more freedom in feature writing. 'These
days, we're drowning in information – lost in a flood of facts – and
we've got to pick our way through it. The novelist can make things
up, which a journalist can't do, but we can use our imaginations
to shape a story. A journalist can craft reality in different ways
and the main thing is trying to convey a sense of what something
was like – nobody realises how difficult that is. If you were to give
someone the task of attending an event then summing up exactly
what happened, they'd realise it's an impossibility. It's only one person's
perspective and that's the real challenge of brilliant journalism.'

Capote influenced a generation of non-fiction writers and David is a great admirer of Gordon Burn, who wrote about Yorkshire Ripper Peter Sutcliffe. Somebody's Husband, Somebody's Son, was an attempt to tell the story of the Yorkshire Ripper from the inside out. Burn spent three years getting to know Sutcliffe's family after the killer's conviction in 1981, turning up night after night to hear stories of the man's early life.

'Public perception of journalists is also something of a stumbling block for the profession. These days, the majority of newspapers appear to be more concerned with the latest exploits of various celebrities than genuine reporting.' But not all journalists get into the industry because they want to ruin people's lives. 'I think respect for journalists always seems to have been at an all-time low – and it certainly is now,' David says.

'In George Orwell's day the whole country was completely different and not celebrity-obsessed. Journalists would deal with issues such as poverty and educating people. I don't see a difference between being an author and being a journalist and I don't think being a journalist is anything to be ashamed of – in fact, it's very necessary in a democracy.'

Orwell had a great sense of purpose as both a journalist and an author. He once wrote: 'When I sit down to write a book, I do not say to myself, "I am going to produce a work of art." I write it because there is some lie that I want to expose ...'

The image of journalists as nothing more than con artists hell-bent on achieving the ultimate scoop is unfortunately one that sticks in people's minds. Renowned British journalist Nicholas Tomalin once wrote: 'All that's needed for success in journalism is rat-like cunning, a plausible manner, and a little literary ability.'

While David says he's never had to use subterfuge to extricate information for an article, there is an argument that, to a certain extent, journalists use everyone they come across while in pursuit of a story. 'In the early Nineties I visited a hospice for people with AIDS and took time get to know people there,' he explains. 'My ability to tell their story was completely through understanding them, getting rid of my ego and putting it into my words. I feel that's the best and most important article I've done, but I didn't feel as though I'd been a vulture or that people had been morally compromised –

even when they were showing me the tapes they would send to their mothers after their deaths. People could point their fingers and say I was being exploitative but, ultimately, we are explaining what somebody else's life is like and that should be what journalism is about.'

In David's opinion, great journalism should transport people to a different place so they, too, can experience the same emotions as the writer. 'There's too little of that because it costs too much money and our culture is getting a bit celebrity-led,' he adds.

History demonstrates many journalists have successfully crossed the barrier between newsprint and the pages of novels, for example George Orwell and Ernest Hemingway. 'It goes right back to the first novelist – Daniel Defoe — who was also a journalist,' says David. 'After that it's just a roll-call of most of the greats: Mark Twain, James Boswell, Rudyard Kipling, William Thackeray. It carries on with people like Norman Mailer and Truman Capote, up to the present day with Colm Tóibín, John Banville and Adrian Nicole LeBlanc.'

David says he could never be like the writers he interviews, in fact, he's in awe of them. Even appearing before crowds, while he did the book festival circuit promoting In Cold Ink, he didn't feel at home. 'Being on the stage is a very unnatural position for me, just as being in front of a radio microphone or a television camera would. I'm always happiest as a fly on the wall – that's my default mode,' he says. 'You just want to try and explain your time on the planet – something about your perception. Although you are coming to it from a more objective direction in journalism, you're still trying to put down on paper what it felt like at that certain moment – so that's common to both journalism and fiction.'

The argument about the similarities and differences between the two disciplines certainly isn't old ground. In November 2007, David Leigh wrote in The Guardian: 'Slow Journalism would show greater respect for the reporter as a patient assembler of facts. A skilled craftsman who is independent and professionally reputable. A disentangler of lies and weasel words ... Aren't such people essential for probing the dodgy mechanisms of our imperfect democracy, and our very imperfect world?'

Perhaps a good way to end this article is with a quote from a review by Peter Conrad about a collection of Scottish novelist Andrew O'Hagan's essays, which appeared in The Observer in 2008: 'If we want to know the truth about the false world we live in, we need to consult the writers of fiction.'

J.A. Cosgrove is a journalist and fiction writer. She studied English Literature and History of Art at the University of Edinburgh and graduated in 2004. She has since gone on to work for a number of publications. She lives in Dundee.

King's Lynn
for Tony Ellis
By Robert Crawford

Here you will find the first name of Vancouver,
How centuries ago he sailed away

From low-lying Old World wharves, leaving behind
A pocket England of residual saints,

Flood-prone and treasured. Each time, on arrival,
I love the rainy friendliness, the endless

Autumn days washed with wishy-washy light,
The muddied, frugal town, a steamrollered

Churchillian remnant, muddled, nodded off,
Grey fields stretched flat, damply attenuated

To cricket clubs, ribbed silt, fogged distances
Still floating on their own in-turned tide,

Keepsakes from the east coast of an England
Whose staunch Vancouver left, and hoisted sail.

Professor of literature and creative writing at the University of St Andrews, Robert Crawford is not only a celebrated poet with six volumes of poetry to his name, but was short-listed for the T.S. Eliot Prize for his collection of poems Full Volume. Professor Crawford is also one of Scotland's most noted scholars, receiving the 2009 Saltire Society Literary Award for his biography of Robert Burns.